HORIZONTAL RUST

HORIZONTAL RUST
a novel
by Ned Russin

Cover design by Andrew Peden
Book design by John Scharbach

First Printing, 2021
ISBN 978-1-7364991-0-8
Shining Life Press
Washington, DC

This is Shining Life Number 33

THURSDAY NIGHT

Lucky for me, Wilkes-Barre is boring. There's nothing on offer here beyond what you'd find anywhere else: movies, bars, parties, restaurants — common time-passing activities that afford a baseline of stimulation and escape from the malaise of suburban living. Possibly, "suburban" is misapplied to Wilkes-Barre, which remains an urban center by some strict definitions. Language in my hometown can be confusing. Like any community in America, we have a self-important, semi-solipsistic lexicon that assigns extraordinary meanings to ordinary words — words like "culm bank" and "creek" that serve to situate ourselves at the center of our own universe. It's nice to know, in any case, that I'm not missing out on anything while I'm trapped inside this hotel for the weekend.

I sit with my mom and dad. We are in a lounge on the ground floor of the Genetti Hotel & Conference Center, a hotel in downtown right off the Square. They laugh and say hello to people they just saw a few hours earlier, when everyone was checking in. Later they will be their business selves but now they are their casual selves — jeans and T-shirts not yet supplanted by collared shirts and khakis.

Two different people occupying each body. But that isn't really the case. I can say that I'm only one person, sitting here beside my dad, and that tomorrow I will sit in a different chair while looking up at him on the stage.

Wilkes-Barre, like much of Pennsylvania, was built around the coal industry. But as the 20th century wore on, the industry evaporated. The wealthy companies and their owners left. Nothing has replaced them or their capital, which underwrote the construction of the city in an image of mountain quaintness befitting the region's topography. The façade has remained ever since the coal barons' divestiture, the essential beaten-down-ness of the place hidden behind an unyielding optimism that is the post-Depression American psyche's default orientation: if we can't make it, it's because we didn't try hard enough. So, in the face of material decline, Wilkes-Barrians went on living and getting dressed up on Sunday and trying to climb up the ladder one rung at a time.

When I say "Wilkes-Barre," by the way, I'm referring to a whole region. I've never lived in Wilkes-Barre proper, and I don't know many people who have. Wilkes-Barre the city is just a small speck of land, an unbustling metropolis. "Wilkes-Barre" the area, though, refers to all the places sitting beyond the shadows of the eight-story skyline. From small suburban towns like the indistinguishable landscapes of Forty Fort or Swoyersville or Luzerne, to pastoral tracts of boringness like Mountain Top or Dallas, out to the woods of Shickshinny or Huntington Mills —"Wilkes-Barre" is a catchall for everything, for post-industrial failures, for transcendental landscapes, for little kids smoking cigarettes, for quads and dirt bikes. For a place that has lost its way.

I was born at Nesbitt Memorial Hospital in Kingston, a leafy suburb right across the Susquehanna River from downtown Wilkes-Barre. The hospital's main entrance was 400 feet from the doorstep of my childhood home. When I was two years old, I was found at the bottom of the basement steps, my fibula spiral-fractured. A spiral fracture is when the bone twists until it breaks. My two-year-old bones had snapped as if they'd had a psychotic episode, too weak to hold themselves together. My mother picked me up and rushed me back to Nesbitt, sprinting across Wyoming Avenue and bursting into the emergency room in hysterics. Because she was a walk-in, we had to sit and wait, my mom trying to maintain a bearing of concerned maternal cool while I tactlessly screamed and cried for what must have been hours. Convenience had given way to consternation. In my defense, though, I was — again — two. This is according to my second-hand memory of early childhood, as compiled from others' stories. Today, Nesbitt is a private psychiatric facility called First Hospital. Kingston is where I grew up and where I went to school. That's the signified when I speak of home.

Since returning to my parents' house after graduation earlier this year, the cardboard boxes having been unpacked and returned to my childhood bedroom, I've found typical hometown nights bleaker than usual. I expected my room to be as I had left it four years before, never mind all the changes to décor I'd observed first-hand upon my many prior returns for school breaks and summers. For my high -school graduation, my mom had made a framed collage of photos from the first 18 years of my life, a family tradition that began with my oldest brother. She hung it in my room after I left for New York, right over my twin-sized bed. It made me feel like I was dead. Or at least a part of me was. A eulogy to the old me. Gone also was the sea-foam green paint I'd picked, as a pre-teen, for my walls. I was to stare, now, at a much more mature shade, some kind of natural cream. My bookshelf still was in its accustomed place, the once-alphabetized and organized stacks now entropic. I'd sit on my bed and try to remember the room from four years before, a more innocent and simpler place, but I couldn't. The memory of the present erased that of the past.

Considered objectively, my nights here weren't materially different than they'd once been. The same opportunities presented themselves, and many of the same people were available to spend time with. We just weren't as close anymore. I'd gone to New York and most of them to Philadelphia. But now everyone had returned home, just like me. It would probably be nice to see them, to catch up. But somehow the prospect felt remote.

Graham, you remember Mr. and Mrs. So and So? my dad asks every time a person comes to the table.

I smile, nod, say, Yeah, of course!

These reintroductions are to people I've seen before, at other SBO conventions, people whose existence was, until tonight, buried somewhere deep inside my brain, the memories of their faces made accessible only by their physical presence, right in front of me. They all stand there while my father and mother sit, bending over so as to not speak too loudly in the public space, reminiscing in jovial tones. We see these people once every four years, except for my father who, because of his role on the executive board, sees them maybe four times a year at meetings in Philadelphia. What they have to talk about beyond the SBO and general niceties, I have no idea.

People continue to enter, and I continue to sit, sinking further into my slouch and nodding my head every time I'm called upon to do so. There's a bar on one side of the room, an outdated but not rundown piece of furniture, the kind of plush-vinyl-trimmed bar you expect to see in a place like Genetti's. No bartender is on duty, so it falls to the attendees to approach the bar, whose surface is replete with bottles of wine, Crown Royal, and Stolichnaya, and help themselves. Almost everyone who pours out a portion of Stoli jokes that it's the most appropriate choice, implying that the imported beverage connects us to our past in some profound way and that drinking it in the present setting is an important cultural exercise, not just as an efficient shortcut to getting drunk in the hotel at 9 p.m. A cooler made to look like a giant Pepsi can stands next to the bar and is filled with Diet Coke.

Standing by herself amid all this is Ollie Hubik, one of the only other non-elderly people here. Ollie, an em-barrassed abbreviation of Olga, is the daughter of Phillip Hubik, a liver-spotted member of the executive board, and his wife, Jane. Phil looks like a string bean, skinny and also always slightly hunched over. I recognize Ollie because, like me, she's always with her parents at the conventions. I watch her pour a cup of Stoli and remain inconspicuous. She's a year younger than me, potentially drinking illegally, and looking content and cool. She's wearing a yellow dress that ends in the middle of her thighs. Her face is round and her shoulder-length hair is tucked politely behind her ears. As I'm staring at her, she turns my way and smiles, her red-painted lips parting to show impressively white teeth. I smile back and nod.

Despite our being at these events together our entire lives, we've never so much as introduced ourselves to each other. I couldn't even classify us as acquaintances. More like familiar strangers. But something has happened since the last time I saw her, four years ago. The physical change that occurred in my life between the beginning and end of college felt normal and natural, but if Ollie is any indication, I'm a wholly different person now. She's still familiar enough that I recognize her, of course, but she seems more adult, her posture confident and certain. Maybe it's just a projection of what I think I lack, but she looks powerful. Maybe I'd be confident, too, if I hadn't moved back home to live with my parents after being denied every job I applied for in New York.

Applying for jobs is what I ought to be doing right now, so I should be happy that I'm here — it gives me a quasi-legitimate reason not to be scrolling job boards and drafting cover letters. I continue to sit and stare at Ollie.

Henry! my father's voice interrupts.

Henry Vanek, a retired elementary school principal from New Jersey, is the president of the SBO. I'm told by my parents that he was a harsh disciplinarian in his professional life (which I assume was par for the course in mid-20th-century childhood education) and that he rules the Organization with a similar temperament. My dad says Vanek enjoys making the tough decisions. He and my father get along well, though my dad's style tends toward leniency, at least as far as family goes.

Vanek purses his lips and sticks his head forward, soundless. The curse of the office of SBO president, going back to Vanek's predecessor, the late Greg Kowalski, is larynx cancer. For over 10 years now, the SBO has been ruled by men who could not speak. Both presidents have (or had, RIP Kowalski) throat backs, those little machines with outdated headset microphones that produce speech in awkward and unempathetic computer tones. But Vanek prefers not to use his, and Kowalski was the same way. (I don't blame them. The modulated voice is hard to make out, especially in crowded rooms, where SBO presidents frequently need to be, and often leads to redundant questions and all kinds of awkward misunderstandings.) Instead, they'd gesticulate and nod, and for events like this it worked just fine. People did most of the talking for them. They'd just agree or disagree, nodding or shaking their heads or, if something really needed clarification, writing down responses in shorthand. They also always had their wives close by to faithfully relay insight or opinions.

Sergei and Bonnie, thank you for everything. It is so great to be in your hometown! Mrs. Vanek says. Oh and look, it's Graham! So nice to see you, honey. How are you enjoying the conference so far?

I stand up and shake hands.

Nice to see you, Mrs. Vanek. And yeah, I'm enjoying the conference. It's been fun so far, I tell her.

This is untrue but necessary, I think.

And you are done with school now, right? she asks.

I am, I say. I am.

Oh congratulations, honey! What's next?

Well I'm looking for jobs still. It's still a little tough looking for work out there. But I'm constantly looking and think I'll figure it out soon.

She turns to my parents. Thank God Henry and I are retired! she laughs. She turns back to me. But I'm sure you will, honey. With a little help from God. You will be all sorted out soon, I'm sure, bright boy like yourself with a degree from a great school.

Thank you, I say.

She pauses and smiles. I think Mr. Vanek wanted to speak with you, didn't you, Henry?

Vanek nods. John Stinton's laughter from the bar cuts through the room. He's at the bar pouring himself a drink. A cup of Stoli, of course. My attention returns to the table, my parents and I sitting with the Vaneks still standing over us. Henry Vanek waves me to him, his expression saying, *Come with me, young Graham.*

Mrs. Vanek takes my seat and I follow Henry out the door. He shuffles along the patterned carpet with a particular lack of grace. The throat-back microphone hangs around his neck like a popstar's as we walk silently along. What could he possibly want to talk to me about? In moments like this, moments where the uncertainty of the future is all but known, my mind drifts to terrible places — to imagined disasters. An unnecessary preparation for darkness. When I get a phone call from my mom at 10 at night, I immediately think she's calling to tell me terrible news, that she's just found my father murdered at home. I wince imagining the bloody scene, but it turns out she's just driving home from the movies and wanted to check in — on speaker phone, of course. My mind revels in its capacity for absurdity in such situations, and even though I know that I'm always going to be wrong, I can't help it. It works in the opposite direction as well. Ollie's smile before, the large and rounded smile displaying one dimple and those brilliant teeth, invoked a lifelong fantasy that begins with my asking her out and continues all the way to our wedding, our buying a house, and the birth of our children, two girls. All of this without, as I say, a single real-life conversation, let alone holding hands.

As it happens, Vanek and I have never spoken in private before, either, and I don't know why we'd need to now. He's going to tell me that he's having an affair with my mother. Or, even worse, he's going to ask me to help the Organization with social media, which my father and I often joke about due to the SBO's perennial inability to stay modern. I'd prefer neither. I continue to follow Vanek in silence through the hallways until we arrive at a small café, now closed. He takes a seat and I follow suit. The small notebook is retrieved from his pants' back pocket and a pen from his shirt pocket.

On the pad he hurriedly scrawls a note, all upper-case. He shows it to me.

I HEARD YOU NEED A JOB

Yeah, yeah, I do actually, I say. My nerves calm somewhat. I am not being reprimanded, at least. I've been applying for jobs since I graduated and haven't had any luck, unfortunately, I say. Hopefully going to hear back from some people soon. A bit of a stretch.

WOULD YOU WANT TO WORK FOR SBO?

I don't like letting people down. I don't like hurting people's feelings. I don't like conflict. And I don't want to work for the Slavic Brotherhood Organization. That is not what I envisioned doing with my life. I have no interest in life insurance, I have no interest in my Slavic heritage, I have no interest in hanging around with a bunch of old people. But I can't say that. I can't flat-out say no. That would be rude.

I haven't really considered it, I say. I don't think there's anything for me at the Organization right now that I'm exactly looking for. Maybe if something came up, but my dad hasn't mentioned anything. I'm just going to keep looking elsewhere for now.

I tangle myself in telling half-truths. I don't mean what I'm saying but the words are coming out regardless. What I should be saying is: no. Categorical. No, I don't want to work at the SBO. But I can't make myself do it. Again, confrontation has never been my strong suit. In school, I'd be one of the few students who actually tried in group projects, taking it upon myself to compensate for others' neglect. I'd think terrible things about my partners. This fucker is too dumb to do the work anyways, probably only got in because daddy paid off admissions. This guy is too that, this that is too this. And then when we'd meet the day before our presentation, to go over all my work, I'd almost feel sorry for them, ashamed for thinking all the terrible things. The hate would dissipate. I would never be able to tell them how I'd felt because I didn't feel that way anymore. Suddenly I wasn't mad or upset. I told myself that they were people and had things going on in their lives and I had no right to act as if what was going on in mine was more important. Human contact always corrected my hatred. Empathy exists face to face.

Is there anything available? I ask.

Vanek starts to write.

GOING TO NEED A SEAT ON EXEC BOARD. SEC TREA-SURER. PHIL HUBIK IS OUT

Why is Mr. Hubik out?

Vanek stares at me.

Phil Hubik was elected to the SBO's Executive Board at the last convention, in 2009. During the elections, which per custom occurred on the final day of the convention, Hubik's wife, Jane, stood up, assumed a prideful upright posture next to her chair, and nominated her husband from the floor, speaking his name loudly enough for everyone in the drab conference room to hear, while Phil sat smugly beside her. What Jane did was as drastic as someone objecting to a marriage. It was cinematic. Vanek had always picked out the board himself and pushed through his ticket with no resistance. He would distribute a piece of paper telling the constituents who they were going to vote for, and because the constituents trusted him and because Stinton's speech always noted how well the Organization was doing, no one had cause to question Vanek's slate of nominees. But when Jane Hubik broke with tacit protocol and nominated her husband from the floor in the year after the country entered its worst economic downturn since the Great Depression, it planted a seed in people's minds that, perhaps, they should do something different, they should promote one of their own. Phil Hubik's character and qualifications were not salient; it was the meta-narrative that resonated. Here was an underdog story of sorts. A hero of the ordinary. Phil had many friends in the SBO, like everyone who's active in the Organization, and on that day in 2009 enough hands went up to fulfill Jane's wishes. The support secured for Phil, this insurgent whom the rank-and-file hadn't realized they'd been waiting for, a seat at the table. The episode had seemed wholesome enough to me, but that's not how Vanek saw it. He believed — this is what my parents told me — that the Hubiks were trying to establish themselves as an SBO prestige family in a bid to shift the balance of power toward the Western PA and Ohio lodges, which had perennially been seen as subordinate to the Northeastern PA dynasty. This was not OK by Vanek. He wielded power and was not going to give it up. He was determined to make of the Hubiks' power-play an example of what happens to those who would challenge his authority. The Hubiks would pay. He had been planning this for four years.

SEC. TREASURER PAYS 13$ K / YEAR. LOW COMMITMENT. GOOD FOR RESUME

$13,000 isn't enough to live on in any city, but it's enough to continue living with my parents in Wilkes-Barre while applying to jobs. My only obligation would be to travel with my dad to Philadelphia — where dinner would be bought for me — one night every few months. I could probably manage that even if I had a full-time job. Regardless, it's a terrible idea. And it's better than anything I have at the moment.

I don't think I'm qualified, Mr. Vanek, I say. I studied writing, not finance or business. I have no real relevant experience.

He turns the page on his notepad.

YOU DONT NEED ANY EXPERIENCE. AND WE NEED YOUNG PEOPLE IN SBO, THIS MAKES US LOOK GOOD, TRUST ME

So Mr. Hubik is going to step down from the seat? I ask already knowing the answer. I don't want Vanek to realize I know about his grudge.

HE DOESNT DESERVE HIS SEAT Vanek writes to me. *I WANT HIM OUT!*

I sit dumbfounded and uncomfortable.

IF YOU AGREE, ILL MAKE SURE YOU GET ON. WE HAVE TO TAKE HIM OUT THOUGH

Does my dad know about this?

NO

I think I should probably talk this over with him, then, I say.

DAD CAN'T KNOW. The period is inscribed with a degree of force that can only indicate angry insistence. He picks his pen back up. *IF YOU TELL DAD ILL KICK HIM OFF BOARD TOO*

NO ONE CAN KNOW

He stares at me, leaning forward with both eyebrows raised.

15

GIVE ME YOUR ANSWER BY TOMORROW NIGHT

Vanek wants me to take part in a purge of the SBO Executive Board. I feel a familiar tingling in the right-hand corner of my upper lip. I'm getting a cold sore. Great.

When I arrived at Columbia to begin my college career, I moved into John Jay, a dorm on the south side of the quad. It sits right next to Butler, the school's biggest and most prominent library, and directly across from Hamilton, where a majority of my first-year classes were. Butler was the cliché to be avoided. The more experienced students spoke of it as if it were an edifying mistake that every undergraduate eventually needed to make: only a young and naïve student would work there, with its overcrowded tables and overwhelming insides, its interior enough to make even the best young scholar feel like a fraud. There were smaller and less congested places to spend one's time, all only a five-minute walk away. I never tired of it, though. I worked in other libraries, sure — the East Asian Library in Kent was a good one, and the blue chairs by the far windows in the music library of Dodge was one of my favorite spots on campus — but when speaking of college, Butler is usually the first thing I think of. It's an embodiment of Columbia: old and ornate and beautiful and standoffish. Butler also notably featured the names of the most important thinkers and writers, as Columbia deemed them, carved into the face of the building. Here were *Homer, Herodotus, Sophocles, Plato, Aristotle, Demosthenes, Cicero,* and *Virgil* staring down at you.

Not only did every student have to read their work as components of The Core — Columbia's compulsory curriculum, whose goal was to make you a good Western citizen — but we had to be reminded, whenever we chanced to go near Butler, that we were attempting to live up to their names.

I had chosen a single room in John Jay. The building's exterior was typical Columbia grandness: worn-in marble stairways leading to traditionally elegant doors that covered up slightly outdated innards. From television and movies, I had gathered that communal living in college was to be avoided at all costs. Learning how to live with one, two, or three other people seemed too daunting a challenge alongside that of learning how to be a person on my own. Luckily, Columbia was one of the few schools that allowed freshmen to live in residence solo, much to my parents' disappointment. They had wanted for me the standard college experience, which I was dead set against. I made a deal with my dad: get into Columbia, get a single dorm. He agreed, never expecting me to get in. My mother was furious. A deal's a deal, I said.

As I unpacked my bags, filling sterile-looking dressers with shirts that would never again be folded as well as my mother had folded them, I looked out over the campus. The room was a small rectangle. Very small. I set up the bed on the wall opposite the window. My mother laid out blue and white bed sheets she'd brought from home. Columbia colors! she said. Directly across from the bed, situated right next to the window, was my desk and chair, both provided by the school, in stereotypical light-grain wood. I brought no posters or decorations with me, save for a family photo my mother had given me of all of us at my high-school graduation. I set the frame up on the back corner of my desk.

I had long expected my admission to be revealed as some sort of prank. It's not that I didn't try hard in high school or do all the things that you need to do to get into a good college. I did it all (constant SAT prep, extracurriculars, AP classes, volunteering, connecting with alums). Still, it seemed to me, an Ivy League degree was of a higher standard than I could meet. When I got my acceptance letter, my dad told me that he was so impressed and proud of me but that he had originally thought I was setting myself up for depression. I asked him what he meant.

I thought you weren't going to get in, he said. Not that I didn't think you could, but it's so difficult to get into a school like that! Columbia, wow! I can't believe it.

In the dorm room with my mom on that first move-in day, I understood how he felt. I felt the same way. I wasn't qualified. Imposter syndrome was not my first cliché. I pushed the chair in front of the window and sat there a long while. Success, I told myself, leads to isolation. It's why the hordes work cheek by jowl in cubicles while the higher-ups get the privacy of the corner office.

Success isn't the only route to isolation, of course. There are plenty of unsuccessful lonely people. Sure, Vanek may be all alone at the top, but look at me. Here I am, unsuccessful as ever, spending a Thursday night in a blank room at Genetti's. The circular tables are set up along the walls, covered in white plastic tablecloths and bearing small bowls of chips and pretzels, whose immanent grease seeps into the skin of every delegate who helps him- or herself to a hearty handful. The convention organizers — no event co-ordinators, these people, barely even party planners — put together this impromptu gathering for the convention attendees who are staying at the hotel and arrived early. The plan was to gather at 9 in this side room, access to which was granted as part of the package deal the SBO had struck with the hotel for the weekend rental of the grand convention room. I helped unstack chairs and place them around the tables a few hours ago.

Graham, you remember John Stinton, right? my father asks. The question brings my attention back to the table and away from thoughts of Vanek and his offer. Stinton, whose nice-ish loafers, Dockers, and summery plaid buttondown flagrantly violate the unannounced casual dress code, stands next to my father with an affable smile, holding a cup of Stoli. He's an oddball at the SBO convention: a non-member. Stinton is an investment-fund manager, whom the SBO retains to make sure that the profits, marginal as they may be, go toward shares in trustworthy and growing companies. The money made from the Organization's small life-insurance policies is taken to the low-risk stock market so that capital may accumulate, albeit at modest rates. Even coming out of the recession, things were still operating smoothly, thanks in part to Stinton. The other, much more pertinent factor was that the SBO recently sold the office it had operated out of for nearly a century. The office, a building on Philadelphia's Spring Garden Street, was three stories of early 20th-century elegance. Not something you'd see in Wilkes-Barre. The building had legal heritage status, which obligated the SBO to keep up the place's antique appearance, at considerable expense. The Organization sold it for more than its appraised value, as the market had started to flirt with normalcy again, and moved to a smaller, more modern office, raising some $2 million in the bargain. According to my father, other fraternal life insurance companies are struggling to stay afloat, but with Stinton handling the portfolio, the Organization's investments maintain a steady growth even though the policies are no longer coming in at the desired volume. I can't imagine there are too many other fraternal life insurance companies, but I've never asked. I guess the SBO is the best, though.

Yeah, how are you doing? I respond, extending my hand. Stinton shakes my hand firmly.

Oh, I'm just happy to be here. Going to have a great time this weekend. Your dad does a great job here with the SBO and all. I'm happy to be here in Wilkes-Barre too! Nice place to have grown up, I'm sure. I heard you're done with school, your dad said? Must be nice.

Yeah, I'm enjoying my time back at home, I say.

Stinton and my father start to speak in increasingly louder bursts. My mother leans over to me.

John and his wife just got divorced a little bit ago, she whispers. He's living the bachelor life now, daddy says.

Ollie is at the bar again pouring herself another drink. I decide now would be a good time to get something myself.

Hey Ollie, I'm Graham.

Hey, I know your name. I'm Ollie. You know that too, she says jokingly.

She knows my name. I smirk.

Just wanted to say hello is all. We've been at these conventions basically our whole lives and I feel like we've never talked or hung out. Which is a shame because I think we're the only people here under 85.

Ha, well, yeah. Then I'm looking forward to getting to talk or hang out with you this weekend.

John Stinton approaches the bar. Hey you two, save some Stoli for the rest of us.

The last time I got a cold sore was two months ago, May 21st, on Class Day. Columbia's graduation is split into two separate ceremonies: the enormous Commencement for all 10,000-some graduates, and the much smaller Class Day for each individual school within the University. Class Day is the much more personal event, where they actually call your name and you walk across a stage and get a placeholder diploma before waiting months to get a real one in the mail. They have speeches by the valedictorian and a notable alumnus (ours was playwright Terrence McNally, who reminded us that our graduation had all the elements of a great drama) and great photo ops — all the hallmarks of a small Liberal Arts graduation despite Columbia's vastness.

There's no origin story for my cold sore. One day in high school, it just appeared, unannounced and unexpected, and ever since then I've had to deal with the embarrassment three to four times a year. Sometimes I get the tingling on my lip just from hearing the words. Early in my college career, the cold sore tended to show up around mid-terms and finals. The crusty red and brown circle would protrude from my face, on cue, when the blue books arrived. That relatively reliable cause-and-effect relationship subsided as I adapted to my schedule. Now the thing is apt to just appear suddenly, at the most inopportune times.

I went to bed on the night of May 20th with a light dancing on my lip. Lying there upon an unkempt bed, I tried to wish it away, mind over body. If I can get to sleep fast enough, I thought, it won't show up. Next morning, there it was, the unwelcome visitor, greeting me in the mirror. I had no choice but to embrace it. I dressed myself in the blue gown, generously steamed by my mother the night before, and descended to the lawn in front of Butler, my last moment as an undergraduate. The stage where we shook President Bollinger's hand and were awarded a commemorative pin was set up opposite the library, its awning to our backs, out of view, as if to suggest that we would no longer have to face those titans of the canon and their august names, though they were still watching over us. We couldn't see them, but they could see us: a perpetual academic panopticon. Graham Mercy, Bachelor of Arts in creative writing. I didn't trip as I walked across the stage. My family cheered. The cold sore shifted up my face as my smile pushed it farther into the corner. A professional photographer flashed a photo.

The Walgreens I'm driving toward is a block away from my high school's campus, Wyoming Seminary. Sem, a century and a half old and stereotypically preparatory, was once a precursor to the regal life among Wilkes-Barre's old industrial elite. Sem's buildings are old and brick-laden, with lush, green grass; its brochures depict those features set against amazing blue skies. The school has both boarding and day students. I was one of the latter, as the campus was only slightly farther from my parents' house than Nesbitt Memorial. The majority of the boarders were international students whom the school had recruited on overseas visits (a time-tested and much-mimicked prep-school tactic that allegedly was pioneered by a Sem faculty member). Officials would travel abroad and pitch the school to wealthy communities, usually with great success. Families sent their kids to receive what they had been assured was the best possible kind of education: private and American. My parents thought the same thing, taking me out of public school after eighth grade, against my wishes. And I guess it worked: I ended up in the Ivy League. But being uprooted from my friends, whom I'd spent eight years with, left me with a kind of bereft feeling, an estrangement from my community, that followed me to college. I lived in the town, but I was alienated from its daily happenings. I was never able to bridge that gap.

Sem was the type of school that made reading *The Catcher in the Rye* feel like it was written just for me, but realistically the prep schools that matter and that Salinger was referencing, capital-P Prep schools, are a little more northern. I didn't know that until I came to Columbia. Exeter, Choate, Groton — these were the schools with real prestige. At Sem, we attempted to be that. We weren't. I didn't realize how far behind we were until I met third- and fourth-generation private-school kids. My school had required collared shirts and fielded a lacrosse team, but it wasn't elite, not like these other places. The students I met in New York from New Hampshire all seemed to be experts in classics, reading the *Odyssey* in Greek and discussing Aristotelian philosophy. How could 18-year-olds be so far apart? After meeting them, I understood Holden Caulfield's desire to run away even more.

Under the fluorescent lighting of the drug store, I move through the aisles, looking for some sort of medicine. Walgreens is a more recent addition to the area, having been built sometime in the early 2000s. It was quickly assimilated into our local culture, giving us something we didn't know we were missing. Because it's the only local business that's open 24 hours, save for the gas stations and the casino that recently opened up, you can find wanderers at Walgreens around the clock. Local characters gather in the parking lot and in the aisles, buying toilet paper in bulk at 2 a.m. For the boarding students at Sem, I'd like to think it stood as a good reminder of Kingston's actual character: not gritty or rude but, all the same, a place where people actually live. Some of the boarders who were old enough would come here for cigarettes and distribute them to younger students at a premium. But mostly you'd see students buying notebooks or folders or index cards, or some sort of neon caffeinated beverage when they had a big test coming up, or maybe an obscene amount of junk food when they were feeling homesick. I usually only popped into Walgreens late like this to get something urgent that I forgot. A Father's Day card on the morning of, some deodorant when I'd already run out, or some medicine to soothe an exploding cold sore.

In moments of stress, I tried to suppress the anxiety and

hopefully uninvite the cold sore. But it was all becoming too much — the job hunt, the lack of response, the failures, the surfeit of time and energy devoted to sending out application after application, rewriting cover letters, and tweaking résumés to include buzz words from job listings. At this point my work-study job now qualified me for everything from "interacting with and assisting faculty and staff" to "independently executing tasks" to "performing daily clerical tasks, such as creating and editing spreadsheets," depending on what I was applying for. I would email professors and ex-employers asking for references, and they'd reply with support and hope, only to tell me a few weeks later that they hadn't heard anything and to ask whether they should still be expecting a call. My failures were now extending beyond myself. My attempt to keep everything within my life — my cold sores, my miserable job search — had never really been private, I began to realize. Everything was visible from the outside, regardless of how close I tried to keep it to myself.

When Vanek pulled me aside, he was trying to capitalize on my failings. He was the alpha wolf and I the deer with a broken leg, separated from my family and vulnerable. He circled around me, sizing me up before going for the kill. A job? Great. I didn't want this job in particular, but at this point I'd consider anything. Kicking out Hubik? Not great. I didn't do well with even minor confrontation, and this was not minor. The thought of Hubik looking me in the eyes after realizing I had taken part in his political assassination was too much to handle.

This was the water that the cold-sore seed drank from. It

drank deep. And before Vanek even had a chance to strike, I was buying ointment that I hoped would alleviate the physical manifestation of my fear.

I locate the small blue and white bottle, near the vitamins for some reason. It comes in two kinds of container, a pump and a squeeze. Both are $20 and contain a measly 0.07 ounces of medicine. Feeling the skin bubbling atop my lip, I imagine its magma spilling over onto my face, distorting my being. The store is now almost completely empty. I go to the counter with shame, clutching the pump bottle in its severe plastic; the clerk doesn't acknowledge the purchase or my face — because, I take it, the two are too obviously, pitifully connected. I ask for no bag and sit in my car in the dark, trying to rip open the packaging. I take my key and insert it into the only gap in the case, the space that accommodates the metal retail hanger. A small crack forms. I proceed to rip with all my strength. The plastic breaks in one jagged piece down the right side of the package, creating a hole barely big enough for my hand. I force the plastic backing down into itself and reach in. There is a broad pain in the center of my right hand, where the hard plastic edge has been forced directly into my flesh, brutalizing nerve endings but drawing no blood.

After pulling down my car's visor and applying the cream to my sore, I stare at myself in the tiny mirror, my hand still throbbing from the stabbing of dull, hard plastic.

FRIDAY

Vanek via Throat Back (*slowly*): Ladies and gentlemen . . . members of the Supreme Council . . . delegates, clergy — welcome. By the authority conferred to me . . . I hereby call the Supreme Convention of the Slavic Brotherhood Organization of the United States of America to order. Please rise while Father Dubinsky leads us in a prayer and a moment of silence for our departed members . . . followed by the Pledge to the Flag led by Michael S. Koval.

Father Dubinsky: Will you please join me in saying the Lord's Prayer, in the name of the Father, Son, Holy Spirit, Amen. Our Father—

Everyone: —who art in heaven, hallowed be Thy name. Thy kingdom come. Thy will be done. On Earth as it is in heaven. Give us this day our daily bread and forgive us our trespasses as we forgive those who trespass against us. And lead us not into temptation, but deliver us from evil.

Father Dubinsky: Oh Lord, grant that I may meet all this coming day and allow it to bring me to spiritual tranquility, grant that I may fully commit myself to Thy holy will. Every hour of this day direct and support me in all things. That what's overdue may reach me in the course of the day. Teach me to accept that it is possible, that all is subject to Thy holy will — my thoughts and feelings and all my words and actions. In all unexpected occurrences, do not let me forget that all is set down from Thee. Grant that I feel straightforwardly and wisely with every member of my family, neither embarrassing nor saddening anyone. Oh Lord, grant me the strength to endure the fatigue of the coming day, and all the events that take place during it. Direct my will and teach me to pray, to believe, to hope, to be patient, to forgive, and to love. Amen.

At this time, we will take a moment of silence for all the departed family members and officers of the Slavic Brotherhood Organization, uh, of the United States of America . . . Thank you.

Koval: I pledge allegiance—

Everyone: —to the flag of the United States of America, and to the republic for which it stands, one nation, under God, indivisible, with liberty and justice for all.

Vanek: You may be seated.

I am home alone. My parents stayed at the hotel to be closer to the SBO members and help out and also to have a bit of a break from regular home life, which seems unnecessary but fine. So I have the house to myself — an odd and particularly suburban sensation. After living in New York for four years, albeit in a dorm, the idea of personal, private space has required some relearning. The proximity of people in

New York and in the dorms made me hyperaware of others' presence. Now, even when I'm alone, I expect that someone can see me through my window and hear my movements through creaky floorboards. It's the sense that, even when you feel completely isolated, you're probably only five feet from someone. It's one thing to feel that way in New York, but at home I risk coming off as paranoid, I remind myself. I lie in bed checking my phone for about 10 minutes, hoping for work emails but seeing only coupons and newsletters. I'm prolonging the start of my morning ritual.

The first item on the to-do list that I mentally compose while pulling my laptop up from the carpet next to my bed and placing it onto my chest is to check LinkedIn. (My computer is a MacBook, not even Pro, that I bought refurbished in 2009, the summer I left for New York — conspicuously outdated only four years later.) I'm almost certain that, here too, I'll have received no updates germane to my job hunt, but I'm sustained in the small act of clicking the bookmark link by the slim chance that something came through and I didn't know it. My LinkedIn account is an exercise in minimalism that I hope reads as humility. The page is sparsely populated with laconic descriptions of my activities from high school (Model U.N., Mock Trial, school newspaper) and Columbia (senior editor at *The Blue and White* magazine, member of the Philolexian Society, board member of Postcrypt) and my achievements (Dean's List a couple of times). The name COLUMBIA staring out from within the screen should be enough, I've often thought, to convince any employer that I'm a hardworking go-getter who is bound to be successful in the most conventional terms. I've not yet landed a single interview.

I have one notification, the little digital flag illuminated with a red mark. I quickly click my way to the next screen.

Chris Cooper's name is listed under job changes. Beneath his name I see "Special Projects Associate at The Certain Group."

I went to high school with Chris, and now he's one of my 189 connections on LinkedIn. We were never that close in high school. A nice-enough guy. We had a few classes together, ate lunch together sometimes, and shared a similar alternative taste in music. I remember we both enjoyed Built to Spill's first album, *Ultimate Alternative Wavers*, which seemed rather a deep cut at Sem. To say we were friends would be a stretch. I didn't know any personal information about him, nothing that would qualify me as an intimate, and he didn't know any about me. We never went to each other's houses. I don't even think I had his phone number (I definitely don't now). Regardless, we were and remain mutually cordial, and he's always acted happy to see me whenever we bump into each other, usually at the Barnes & Noble — for some reason the most notorious accidental run-in spot in Wilkes-Barre.

One night last winter break, I was browsing the magazines when I turned the corner and saw him there, *Rolling Stone* in hand.

Graham! he said. His excitement struck me as unusual given that we hadn't been in touch, save for run-ins like this — circumstantial, not purposeful — for nearly three years. How've you been? he asked.

Hey, yeah, I extended my hand pulling myself towards

him. Nice to see you. I'm doing well, how about you?

I'm doing pretty all right, thanks. Just home for Christmas, you know. Nice to have a few weeks off because this last semester was a lot. I did 17 credits and worked an internship. He rolled up the *Rolling Stone* as if he were about to hit a dog with it, and then tucked it under his armpit. I put my copy of *The Paris Review* back on the shelf. How's everything in New York? Columbia going well?

Yeah, New York's great. It's a lot different than Wilkes-Barre, obviously. But I try to treat it the same.

Chris laughed, a bit too quickly. How do you mean?

Oh . . . I guess I don't try to get caught up in all the New York-ness of New York. I'm not trying to go out to a new spot every night. Restaurant, club, shop — whatever. I go out when I feel like it and try not to feel bad when I don't. Growing up here, there's never anything to do. Probably why we're both at Barnes & Noble at 9 p.m. on a Friday. But that doesn't bother me. I don't always feel the need to do something in New York just to do it.

Wow, that's a unique way to look at it. Some of my buddies at Villanova grew up in like West Chester — New York, not PA — and would go hang out in Manhattan on the weekends and they just told me how out of hand it gets. We are always trying to plan a trip there, but, you know, as I said I've just been swamped with school stuff. If I make it in, I'll be sure to hit you up.

I couldn't possibly overstate the awkwardness of this conversation. Excruciating. We were attempting to be friends but we were not. We hadn't been before and we would not be in the future. The timbre of my voice was tense and

33

uneven, very different from how I knew my voice should sound. I felt as if I were on the set of a soap opera, playing a character based on myself, reciting hackneyed dialogue. Yeah, please do, I said. Always good to see a familiar face when I'm up there. What's your major again? Sounds like it's no joke.

Business, he said. And you're doing English?

Creative writing, I said.

That makes sense! Very cool! You going to write a book or something? Or work as a journalist?

Honestly, I have no idea. I'm just trying to sort that stuff out later.

Our conversation slowly, inevitably decomposed, and Chris's existence returned afterward to deep storage in the back of my mind. Today, though, his having announced on-line that he has a job, complete with a formal title, while I sit here in my parents' house, alone, feels like a gratuitous, micro-targeted attack. I know I shouldn't compare myself to others but I can't help it. What's a Special Projects Associate anyway? He can be one and I can't? I went to Columbia.

My computer closes and returns to the floor.

I get out and head to the bathroom to perform simple acts of hygiene. I get two new daily contacts out of their blue box and delicately shove my fingers toward my eyes, suctioning tiny pieces of plastic onto them, and am suddenly able to see again. I apply the shaving cream to my face and smooth it out evenly before dragging the razor, old and wet, over the contours of my face. As I shave above my lip, I remember that I have a cold sore. I shouldn't have taken away the millimeter of sparse hair, I realize. I should have left it as a diversion. It's too late now. Yesterday's events come back to me. The job offer. The plot against Hubik. Ollie.

Vanek's proposition has invoked a great many anxieties. The most obvious is that I have to take part in kicking an old man out, who I'm not even sure deserves it. But then I think about Ollie. Ollie in her yellow dress. I have a crush on her now.

I'm like everyone else on Earth in that all my crushes are debilitating psychic episodes that yield intertwining fantasies of humiliation and affection: the sappiest, most unrealistic scenes of love adulterated by horrible visions of the love object laughing in my face. Within seconds of picturing Ollie, I start rehearsing lines, deconstructing my posture, working up what I hope will be a winningly inaccurate representation of myself, something much more appealing than what's looking back at me in the mirror this morning: the disheveled hair and crust on the insides of my eyes, the putrid stink coming from my mouth, the small scar on my chin where hair never grows, and, of course, the recently detonated cold sore on my upper lip. The cold sore — red, crusty, and obstinate — returns my stare and laughs. I finish shaving. I miss the same spot I always miss, above the right corner of my lips. I go back over it. I navigate around the cold sore carefully, using the edge of the blade so as to avoid cutting the wound open. I check my phone.

The buffet is out if u want to come here, my dad texts me. Meeting doesn't start until 10. U can make it if u want.

thanks I think I'll come over, I respond. see you soon.

I quickly finish my routine, showering and applying deodorant and brushing my teeth, spending a little bit of extra time brushing my tongue with the back of my toothbrush, gagging myself with every harsh stroke, just in case I get to talk to Ollie again.

I leave through the back door.

I don't have a house key on my keyring anymore. My parents graciously let me keep my car — a 2004 Subaru Outback, white with cream canvas interior and 130,000 miles — throughout my time in college, and I just left the keys at home, they being of no use in New York. One time I came home and the house key was gone off the ring, just like that. I felt bad about the car. It just took up space on the street or in the driveway except when I would use it over winter or summer break, my parents having to move it from one side to the other every week for street cleaning. My dad insisted that he liked having the car around for snow storms; it handled great in winter weather, he said. But I still felt like I was burdening them. So I never asked for the house key back. I switched to using the keypad lock on the back door.

My car guilt worsens if I let myself think about how much money is required for upkeep. For the car itself. For gas, insurance, yearly inspections. The concept of money, the sheer amount of money it takes to live a life, was something I didn't fully understand until my college career. My parents had a deal with their kids: they would pay for undergrad tuition and we would be responsible for any graduate or professional degrees. The tuition at Columbia was not cheap. The room and board — not cheap. Nothing, in fact, was cheap. Even the blue gown that we were required to buy for graduation was $150. We're talking about New York, after all. The city erases your sense of normalcy. Not until you return to Pennsylvania, where the prices are cut almost in half (not just the prices, but the lifestyle expectations, too), do things fall back into perspective. Nevertheless, you've come to accept what you have to deal with if you want to live in New York. If you want food, if you want to see a movie, if you want to do anything, you better be willing to cough up $20, minimum. My parents, to their credit, were happy to pay their share of the freight. And this felt normal to me. It took a nationwide economic collapse to teach me otherwise. I began to realize, toward the end of my college career, how much debt they'd incurred on my account, so that I might simply . . . learn. An immense guilt fell upon me. How would I ever actually pay them back?

I had grown up upper-middle class, a way of life that Columbia gave me the tools to critique. I learned to see through the bourgeois lifestyle I'd been born into. So many of the comforts I had accepted as universal, reliable facts of life were actually social constructs built on a foundation of unfairness. I came to these conclusions through coursework and in-class discussions that my parents paid for, all while the country assessed its own failures and mistaken assumptions in the face of the Great Recession. As the scales fell from my eyes, I tried to cultivate a magnanimous view: I couldn't change my upbringing and, even if I could, I owed it to my parents to recognize that they had worked to build up their wealth and creditworthiness for the sole and express purpose of providing my siblings and me with as happy and fulfilling a life as possible, to afford us opportunities that they themselves hadn't had. Unconditional love is mortgaging your house — whose value had accrued on the updraft of global credit markets that exist for no reason other than to propagate indebtedness — in order to collateralize a student loan for your son, with no expectation of seeing any of that money ever again.

I walk into Genetti's at 9:30. The humidity outside, thick and unavoidable, is quickly forgotten inside the hotel. I walk through carpeted hallways, taking repetitive turns to find the convention room. My mother sits outside the room at the registration table. She is there with one other woman I recognize behind various stacks of paper and amid several boxes.

Good morning, sir. Welcome to the convention, my mother jokes.

Good morning and thank you for having me.

On the table in front of Mom there's a piece of paper designating that she's handling "Last Names N-Z." Those who have "Last Names A-M" are to address the woman next to her. I step in front of the latter.

Mercy, I know. What's your first name again, hon? she asks.

This is Graham, Mary, my mom responds. My youngest. I nod and smile.

All right, OK, Mary says, furiously flipping the five pages back and forth. Ah, I found you. She places a red X next to my name.

My mother reaches behind and gets a bag with my name tag clipped onto it. Printed on the tag are my name (Graham Mercy), lodge number (110), and delegate number (48), as well as the SBO logo. A backstage pass that doesn't get you into any desired spaces. The bag, a black tote with "SBO: Established 1913" printed on its front, contains a folder with the program and various reports to be discussed, a business-card-size calendar with a religious icon on the backside, a pocket-size 2014 planner, a light-up luggage tag, a Christmas ornament featuring a typically Eastern Orthodox flat-faced Jesus, two SBO pens, a bottle-opener keychain, SBO post-it notes, an SBO pamphlet explaining their benefits, and two small magazines touting what to do in Wilkes-Barre, PA.

I put my name tag on and walk into the room.

The conference room becomes real as I open the door into the space. I see the chandeliers and the tables, the stage, a lectern, an American flag. On an easel behind the Executive Board's table, I see a large gold-leafed icon of two saints, one of whom is St. Alexis of Wilkes-Barre — a completely unrealistic likeness, an anti-Renaissance ideal: flat and di-mensional with pointed features and pious upturned palms. The banner bearing the SBO logo hangs with evident pride. My internal map expands slightly as I take in all the room's visual information, but I know that the image, fresh and vivid for the moment, will soon fade into itself.

The point of a hotel conference room is to provide a polite and tranquil background, to comfort you without distract-ing you from doing what you came to do. Like a casino. It's a place that tries to make it as easy as possible to pass an impossible amount of time. The carpet features colors and shapes in some sort of non-linear mess whose pattern reveals itself only as you get farther and farther away. The walls are bland, textured cream. There are no windows but there are small, quiet air vents built into the ceiling, pumping in AC. There are two columns with four rows of long tables, each with a set of nice rolly chairs, the spaces between them roughly uniform. In front of each seat someone has placed a photocopied and stapled program of the weekend's events. Roll Call, National Anthem, Introduction, President's Opening Remarks, Report of Finances, Membership Report, etc. The program — a set of five, one-sided pages of natural-colored 8.5" x 11" cardstock — prominently features the SBO logo, in all its pixelated glory, on the cover page: two shaking hands superimposed on an American flag above an Orthodox cross (the one with the extra, smaller horizontal hatch mark above the main crosspiece and a diagonal one below). Underneath, the program states its purpose: *Slavic Brotherhood Organization: Celebrating 100 Years of Fraternal Life Insurance From 1913-2013. Supreme Convention, July 19-21, 2013. Genetti Hotel & Conference Center. Wilkes-Barre, PA.*

There's an impossibility about rooms you haven't yet entered. Never can I accurately imagine what a place will look like, how it will feel. But as soon as I step foot inside, it seems natural and normal. It takes my seeing it to make it real. It's like the silent tree falling in the forest: even if you *assume* that the tree makes a sound, you won't *know* that it does unless you're on hand to hear the crash in person. No phenomena without corresponding consciousness. I recognize that I'm describing a radically self-centered outlook, everything just an extension of the ego. It isn't real to me until *I* see it. What's behind me might not even exist. I used to spend hours in my parents' basement arguing this proposition during Friday-night sessions of recreational sophistry with my high-school friends. Absence of evidence is not evidence of absence, they'd say. The world doesn't revolve around us, even if our concept of it does, they'd argue. I wrote this off until one day at Columbia my Intro to Statistical Reasoning professor wrote on the board ABSENCE OF EVIDENCE IS NOT EVIDENCE OF ABSENCE. I wrote it in my notebook and drew a star next to it, remembering all the times I had tried to refute it. I hadn't changed my opinion on that, it just seemed like something that you had to believe in. What I can tell myself that I know still depends on my position relative to my environment, but that doesn't mean I disappear into my surroundings or that they disappear without me.

The bottom of the ocean and Glendo, Wyoming, might as well be the same place: a deep and unknowable void somewhere between infinite possibility and nothingness. Like explorers en route to the New World, we let our minds run wild with the possibilities insinuated by places-not-yet-seen; meanwhile, the places are probably pretty normal. Maybe even boring.

The conference room on the first floor of the hotel has existed my entire life, about a mile from where I was born and grew up. I'm sure it was renovated at some point in time, but the guts of the room were there before I was alive, and the building has stood ever since on a street that I've driven many times over. It's one of those streets whose names I often forget and may never have known. If you asked me how to get to Genetti's, I probably wouldn't be able to tell you, but if I got in my car and drove, I could find my way without even thinking about it.

Dad: Thank you, Mr. President, and welcome everyone. Uh, just a few procedurals at this point, as we have discussions on different matters. It's important that you identify yourself with your name and your delegate and lodge number. Those last two are located on top of your name tag. So if you stand up to speak, please say those three things so we know who is talking. We don't know everyone. And with that, as we proceed, Phillip Hubik will have roll call of the officers.

Hubik: Good morning. Uh, President Henry Vanek . . . here. Vice President Sergei Mercy.

Dad: Present.

Hubik: Secretary Treasurer Phillip Hubik, here. Auditor Simon Hanek, Jr.

Hanek: Here.

Hubik: Auditor Martin M. Koval.

Koval: Here.

Hubik: Auditor Matthew Korbel.

Korbel: Present.

Hubik: Director Michael S. Koval.

Koval: Here.

Hubik: Director Arnold Levitski.

Levitski: Here.

Hubik: Director Gerald Malik.

Malik: Here.

Hubik: Director Keith Witkiewicz.

Witkiewicz: Here.

Hubik: Legal Counsel Andrew Sojka.

Sojka: Here.

Hubik: Thank you, gentlemen.

Dad: Thank you.

Christopher Vanek: You forgot me.

Hubik: Christopher Vanek. Sorry, Chris. A lot of Vaneks up here.

Dad: Thank you. Now can we have the report from the credentials committee. Michelle Vanek.

Michelle Vanek: Good morning, everyone. There are 66 delegates present.

Dad: Thank you. With 66 delegates present, I now declare there is a quorum present to proceed with our convention.

At the back of the room, a buffet is set up in silver chafers with small fires lit underneath, the closed lids containing warmth against the air conditioning. I go through the line, preparing a small plate — a bagel, some fruit, a scoop of hash browns — eyeing up the seating arrangement the whole time as if I were in a high-school cafeteria. I take a seat in the back row, my body falling comfortably into the navy depth of the rolly chair's canvas, my feet shuffling underneath the desk's faux wood grain. Bodies are still filtering in slowly, stopping and conversing at the ends and middle of each aisle. Handshakes and hugs are exchanged, creating a positive, familial energy that belies the curmudgeonly appearance of the typical delegate. Some people wear T-shirts and jeans. One person even has a ponytail and is wearing a sleeveless Harley-Davidson shirt. But for the most part the dress is polite and conservative. Their collective roundness is the attendees' most noticeable feature, surpassed only by their physically manifested crotchetiness. I am dressed in a light-blue Brooks Brothers oxford shirt and a pair of dark-washed Levi's, purposefully ignoring the summer heat outside and embracing the AC. The chair's wheels under me move back and forth aimlessly, guided by my absent-minded direction. The meeting is set to begin at 10 a.m.

With the entire Organization assembled, most of the faces in the room are still familiar to me. I recognize them from the previous conventions. The 2009 convention, the summer I graduated high school, was in Philadelphia; the one before that, in 2005, was in Pittsburgh; and 2001 was Wilkes-Barre as well. I had been to all the conventions as part of a weird recurrent pseudo-family-vacation, a work trip passed off as fun. Before his recent promotion to Vice President, my father served as the Organization's Legal Counsel for as long as I can remember, and my mother always had a paid position at the conventions through him. The Slavic Brotherhood Organization was founded in 1913 as a life insurance company by and for Slavic immigrants, those coming from Russia, Poland, Ukraine, etc. A large Slavic population settled in Northeast PA and worked in the coal mines, only to end up dead with little to no savings for their families. There are stories of men dying in the mines and the company simply leaving their bodies on the porches of their homes, to be found by their families when they opened the door to go out for groceries or check the mail. The SBO collected money and distributed it to the grieving families, but the Organization was only made available to the Slavs; hence the fraternal part of fraternal life insurance. It was like a union for an ethnically specific cohort of the dead and their kin. The Organization was sustained through the network of Eastern Orthodox churches, but as the significance of mine work dwindled and the members subsequently began to see improved quality of life, the SBO's necessity diminished yet it has persisted. The main office is filled with black and white photos of large meetings of a previously dedicated group, but the Organization's position in modernity is a barely functioning website and a rapidly declining membership. The conventions' purpose is to make members think otherwise. In the past, the whole family would go to a hotel for a weekend and enjoy the festivities.

My father's grandfather Grigory came over from somewhere in the Carpathian Mountain region. I'm pretty sure he came from what is now modern-day Poland, but his side of the family still identifies as Russian. The story about Grigory is that he was a poor farmhand who saved up enough to move to the United States, but he didn't want to go alone. So he decided to ask for the farmer's daughter's hand in marriage. He paid for her ticket to the States upon receiving a conditional acceptance: if she didn't like him, she would go back to the Motherland. It would be a nice vacation at the very least. At Ellis Island, their last name,

Mirsky, was anglicized to Mercy, the immigration agent bestowing American virtue at a stroke, and the family decided to settle in Northeast Pennsylvania as Mr. and Mrs. Harry Mercy. Their union proved out after all: the original American Mercys had something like 12 children. My dad was born some time later, at the end of one war and right before the start of another, although of course the same can be said for any year picked at random for the greater part of the 20th century. Decades later, as my father became an adult, he took up teaching to avoid the draft, but after a year decided that he would rather go to war than teach children. Luckily for him, he found out that his flat feet made him undraftable. Shortly after, he entered law school, and his career as an attorney started sometime in the '70s. He and my mother met a decade later, after both of their first marriages fell apart. They were married in the early '80s, settling down within a 20-mile radius of their birthplaces. I always assumed my family had taken on the Mirsky's Russian identity because the only traditional things we did were Russian — having a Christmas party on January 7th, having a 12-course peasant's meal on Christmas Eve, licking a piece of salt on Easter — but we were far from Russian, even though my mother knew the ancient words to the songs we sang for birthdays and weddings. *Mnog hia letta.* God grant you many years.

Despite my vague familiarity with the SBO and its conventions, this year, 2013, was my first time attending in an official capacity. Before, my mom, brothers, aunt, and I would just go to the movies, mall, or hotel pool the whole day until whatever nightly cultural event happened. My mom would leave after roll call with no questions asked, despite her paid role. It was a perk of being SBO royalty, I suppose. I didn't know what happened in the meetings and I didn't care. I was on vacation, I couldn't be bothered with the nuances of fraternal-life-insurance finance. But now, in my adulthood, I bear the title of *delegate*, which strikes me as meaningless. In theory, my purpose is to act as a voting representative on behalf of my lodge, using our successes and failures to advocate for our vision for the Organization and for our small local unit. In practice, I'm a seat-filler. The convention is meant to educate the members on the last four years, how the memberships are doing and where our assets lie; state where we hope to be in the next four years; and then vote a new board in to help ensure those changes. I am merely here to pass whatever Vanek wants. Delegate status entitles me to a $600 fee for the weekend. It's all a ruse.

I find Ollie but she is sitting with her family towards the middle of the room. We make eye contact and she smiles and waves, her plate empty in front of her. She is on the outside of the aisle, saving no room for me. Phil's next to her, sitting erect and proud. I imagine he's enjoying sitting in the crowd because he knows he will be up on the stage in just a half an hour. It's like the nobility seeing how the other half live, how they themselves lived just moments before, remembering how bad it was, and realizing how great their new life is. Why would Phil ever go back? He's got a seat at the front table now.

Ollie turns to her parents, says something out of earshot, stands up, and walks over to me. I move my chair back assuming that she's coming to talk to me, hoping to make it obvious that I'm excited to see her. Now free, my hands become objects of awkwardness, shifting and tensing. My back to the buffet, I place my left palm delicately on the table and put my right hand in my pocket to make myself seem calm. I balance my left ankle on my right heel and lean back into the chair. My position is forcefully working against gravity and forcefully awkward. It's too late to change it now. I become aware of my cold sore, again. I quickly yank my hand out of my pocket and rest it on my chin, my thumb slyly attempting to cover up my illness.

Hey Graham! Ollie says as she approaches. Good morning.

Oh hey. How's it going? How was your night here?

It was fine. I just went to bed early. I don't know what there is to do here really.

Yeah that's about all there is to do, actually. It's incredibly boring here, sorry.

She laughs. Without thinking, I move my hand from my face back to my pocket. I see her eyes zero in on my lip. My cold sore tingles as if to acknowledge it's happy someone has noticed it.

Yeah, sorry, I woke up with a cold sore, I say, trying to self-deprecate it out of the way.

Her laughter turns to shame, as if she feels sorry. No, no! I get them too, I know how annoying they are. Don't worry. I wasn't staring.

It's annoying because I get them when I'm stressed out or

nervous, which lately has just been all the time.

She shifts awkwardly again, using the opening I've given her. What are you nervous about?

Oh sorry, I've been applying for jobs for months now, since before I graduated, and still haven't even gotten so much as an interview.

I'm sorry. That must be rough.

Yeah it's not very fun, hence this, I say, pointing at the eruption on my lip.

We laugh.

Please don't let me stop you from eating, by the way. I don't want to stand between anyone and breakfast.

No it's fine. Do you want to sit down and keep talking before the meeting starts?

Oh yeah, sure.

The awkwardness, this brand new awkwardness, it now occurs to me, could be the result of her having picked up on my inchoate crush and consequently feeling strange, either because she feels the same way or, much worse, because she doesn't and is embarrassed for me. It doesn't matter at this point. She takes a seat in the back row, joining me. The room is loud with other people talking and catching up.

So what kind of jobs have you been applying for?

Practically anything. Entry-level gigs doing marketing, publicity, editing, writing. I applied for some freelance writing jobs and didn't hear anything back. I even looked into applying for a job at my old high school to be a teacher. It's a private school and you don't really need any sort of master's degree to teach. But nowhere has gotten back to me at all.

It's tough. It's really tough. I don't know how to navigate it. I'm only a junior. I wish I had some advice for you. Have you tried internships?

Well I didn't do any internships in college because I wasn't really planning on doing the whole standard career thing, I had intended to pursue an MFA in creative writing, that's what I did my undergrad in, but I've decided against it. So now I was thinking about applying for the last of the fall internships still up, to see if I could land any of those and turn it into a job. But it seems kind of demoralizing to have a college degree and be an intern. I don't even know if I can do some internships, since I'm not a student anymore. I pick at my plate. I'm sorry, that sounded rude and entitled. I don't mean it like that.

Oh no, don't worry, I know you're not like that.

How could she know how I am? I wonder.

Well thanks, I say.

Have you been applying for jobs in New York or here at home?

How'd you know I was in New York? I ask.

Oh my parents told me.

Right. Sorry, not trying to be intrusive.

We've never spoken before this moment and yet we're familiar with and know things about one another through our parents' involvement in the Organization.

I've been applying for jobs in both. I'd really like to get back to New York. I don't know what I could do here, really. I mean I don't know what I could do anywhere, but there aren't like companies here to work for, it feels like. There's not really any industry in Wilkes-Barre or anything.

If I were a lawyer or a doctor, I'd be fine, but I don't think I'm going to do that. Unless I somehow land that teaching gig, but that's not really my plan. There's not really anything for me here, but there's a lot in New York. Unfortunately, they just don't seem to be hiring. Or maybe they're just not hiring me. I'd take anything at this point. I pause. Do you like art at all? I ask her. Like painting and stuff.

Uh, a little, why?

Do you like abstract expressionist stuff at all? Jackson Pollock and whatever, the kind of random-looking paintings with just paint everywhere and random lines and stuff?

She laughs. No, not really. I don't know what I'm supposed to get out of it.

Oh yeah, I have no idea what anyone is supposed to get out of anything. I think that's kind of the point of those paintings. But anyway, there's this artist, he's actually born and raised in Wilkes-Barre, his name is Franz Kline. He was in that crew of people, Pollock and them. Here let me show you.

I pull my phone out of my pocket. I google Franz Kline and pull up photos of massive paintings on the tiny screen. The majority of the paintings are a mostly dirty, accidental-looking white, which is broken up by long, linear black streaks that move across the canvas. Some lines start at the edges and work their way inwards and some just appear in the middle. Most of the work consists only of white and black. There's even less to grab onto than with a Jackson Pollock. We both stare at the screen. I swipe to the next image, another white and black painting with thick lines, but this one has landscape orientation. And the next one, more

51

white and black lines. The lines seem to become harsher and harsher with every image.

This is Franz Kline. I don't know if I'd say I understand it either. I only got into it a year or so ago but I really enjoy it now.

How do you get into something like this? she says, smirking at me. I offer a polite chuckle. I'm kidding, really. Explain it to me, maybe I can like it if I know what's going on.

Well that's the thing, I don't know what's going on. Like I don't think I could relay anything about the meaning of the paintings. Kline doesn't want that either, he wanted you to view the painting and put your own ideas onto it rather than have some pre-established cultural idea dictate your interpretation for you. I don't even know if the paintings are any good or not. I mean they must be, since they're in museums, but that's not what attracted me. It's more about Kline's story. I put my phone down. So we have this class at school called Art Hum — Art Humanities, it's called — and it's like an art history, appreciation class wrapped up into one. Western art though, only western art. You start with the Parthenon in Greece and work your way up to like pop art. It's a required course so everyone has to take it to graduate, but it's taught by PhD candidates doing art history, and they tailor it slightly to their interests so every section is slightly different. Every class takes a field trip or two to see the art you're discussing in real life, and when we got to more modern art, which was my professor's area of interest, we went to the Museum of Modern Art. Have you been there?

No I never have, actually.

It's great, you should go. It was cool because it was like a free guided tour, and I realized I like the more modern stuff, maybe starting with like Monet and Van Gogh and all that stuff. The realistic stuff from Renaissance masters didn't move me because it seemed impossible, in a way. Like those paintings are just too good, they're almost devoid of humanity they're so realistic. But this stuff . . . this stuff felt tangible in a way that the art before it wasn't. It felt like I could do it. I know I can't, but it was relatable. That's more the right word: relatable.

I pause. She nods. I continue.

So we're in this one room in MoMA and I see one of these paintings, looks the same as any of the ones here on the screen: nonsensical white and black lines moving and intersecting throughout the canvas. I go up to read the information plaque about it. That's probably one of the first things I do when I'm in a museum, look at the artist to see if I should spend time on it, depending if I recognize the name or not, which I admit is a bad habit because I don't usually spend time looking at something I'm not familiar with unless it really strikes me. Anyway, I see that the guy was born in Wilkes-Barre, PA. Born in Wilkes-Barre and died in New York. I lose it. Seriously, I just lose it. I'm talking to people in class, telling them all about Wilkes-Barre and how it's amazing that this guy made it out of there and into the MoMA. How it's a small town that no one gets out of and whatever. I don't really know how to explain the feeling, it was almost like justification of your existence, or an acknowledgement of it, at least. My classmates must've thought I was crazy.

She laughs.

So after leaving the museum I get a little obsessed. I was just reading about him and getting into his art, even though it still kind of all looks the same to me. I wanted to know about his experiences in Wilkes-Barre. Franz's dad killed himself when Franz was just a kid. His mom remarried and just shipped him off to boarding school, and eventually Franz ended up in New York after college, and that's where his art career took off. He died young, in his early 50s, I think, but he died in New York. I wondered if he ever came back home, to Wilkes-Barre. Probably not. It seemed like a place marred with sadness, though, so I doubt that he did come back. But I feel that real sadness in his work. Something about the sparseness of the work and the contrast in colors. But there's a chance that we occupied the same spaces 50 years apart. Sorry, I'm talking too much, I say.

No, no! It's fine. I like this. I like hearing you explain it.

I kept reading about Franz, though, and I came across this quote and I thought it was maybe the only real key to unlocking his work. He said something about how he paints the white as well as the black. The white is just as important, he said. I thought that was really cool.

What does that mean?

I think it means that the white's not just a background. The white isn't just something that exists to make the black lines stand out or to be painted on top of — they're both there, existing at the same time on purpose. It's not two ideas in opposition or one less important than the other. They're . . . the same thing. So when you look at the paintings you have to be sure to not just look at the black lines. That's all I looked at, at first, how they intersected and moved, totally ignoring the white. You have to look at the whole painting, though. It's not background and foreground, it's just one even space.

I think I get it, yeah. That sounds interesting.

Yeah I like it a lot. But oh! Yeah but the whole point of talking about Franz Kline wasn't really to talk about his art, but more about the fact that he was born in this town but lived and worked and died in New York. It kind of reaffirmed my idea that in order to do it — to like make it, especially when I wanted to be a writer exclusively — you couldn't do it in a small town. And then to see someone make it from Wilkes-Barre and to die in New York and have their work on display in the MoMA was proof that it was possible for someone like me to do it. Someone from not even just the middle of nowhere but from the same nowhere I was from. I thought that was really inspiring. It made me want to live in New York for real after that, not just in a dorm. I was applying for a lot of jobs there, yeah, but nothing happened. And it doesn't make any sense to live in New York when you don't have a job, so I couldn't justify living there just to look for work. So I moved home. I'd like to get back there but it seems almost impossible right now. I had to readjust that idea. I don't want to be a writer now anyway, so I guess it doesn't apply to me anymore. Maybe I'll break the rules and show that you don't have to leave home to make it, but it feels like if I stay I'll just end up doing the same thing as everyone else around here. I'm not sure where I'll end up. For now, though, it's Wilkes-Barre.

After eating breakfast, I bus my own plate, delicately placing the remains in a dark plastic bin next to the buffet. The room continues to fill. Ollie has left and returned to her family, and now I am all alone, just waiting for the convention to start.

My father approaches me, wearing his Bell's-palsied smile, walking alongside a man in a seafoam-green jacket and matching Miami Dolphins tie, a soft leather briefcase in his large, hairy hands, his clenching jaw exposed through his goatee and a single vein protruding from the dome of his wax-effect bald head. I stand up from the rolly chair and extend my hand.

Good morning, I offer, shaking my father's hand with mock formality.

Good morning! my dad responds, his voice deep and round, booming with assurance and authority. You ready for an exciting day?

Yep, yep.

We chuckle somewhat awkwardly. Both my dad and I know this is a joke, but I'm unsure where the joke ends and where seriousness begins. The whole convention — this room, the speakers, the program, and especially the check I was promised at the end of it — seems like an elaborate practical joke, one much different than my admission to Columbia. For what was the reward? The dog and pony show of the convention doesn't matter, and I assume other people know that. But the formalities of our exchange are like a satire in that they acknowledge an underlying, un-changeable truth that's difficult to discuss except by joking about it.

My father, being of his generation and the attendant mindset, was my father first. His parenting and personal style was, I always assumed, influenced by the fact that his father had died unexpectedly when he was 15. We never much talked about the loss, but I gather it instilled in him a set of values that are still important to him all these years later. The value of education (Your education is the only thing I can give you that can't be taken away, he'd often say) coupled with the value of hard work — these he took espe-cially seriously, believing as those of his generation tend to that grit and intellectual curiosity are the principal means by which the son of a plumber becomes a successful lawyer. If this aftermath of the great '08 crash should have taught us anything, it's that the Protestant ethic doesn't necessarily move you ahead. But my dad, like his contemporaries, has been forgivably slow on the uptake. To his credit, he's no Puritan: he believed his kids' success ultimately depended on his providing the right combination of support and au-tonomy. He didn't put much focus on his children's careers as such, affording us the opportunity to make mistakes. My parents cared that we did well in school and that we tried, but they also allowed us room for idealism. We didn't have to be lawyers, even though my oldest brother was now in law school. We could be what we wanted. We just had to try. It was a limitation and a freedom simultaneous. It's how I ended up wanting to be a writer and later opting out. When I arrived at Columbia, I saw that the Reference Room in

Butler bore an inscription of a Francis Bacon quote above the cliché Ivy League archway: A Man Is But What He Knoweth. Dad would've been proud.

Hey, Dad, did you talk to Mr. Vanek last night?

Yeah, of course. Got everything sorted for the convention.

My coup allusion is lost on him, unless he's playing the fool perfectly. In either case, I am on my own.

This is Matthew Korbel, my dad says. He's a board member. This is my youngest, Graham.

Korbel's lips move behind his goatee. Your dad's got a lot of nice stuff to say about you. Columbia grad, right?

Yeah I just graduated in May.

That's great, yeah, congratulations. Really amazing school there. It's impressive. I wish I could have went to a school like that when I was in college. What did you major in again?

These days, I thought a lot about my decision to major in creative writing. In my youthful optimism, I decided that I would devote myself to the craft, ultimately completing some larger body of work, maybe a book of short stories or, ideally, a novel, before matriculating to a top-tier MFA program and making friends with sweater-wearing professors and glasses-wearing students, later making it as a Big Name writer living in a beautiful NYC pad, where I'd have amazingly profound conversations with my writer and artist friends about books, music, and movies. I imagined my editor writing me an apology letter, saying, Graham, you were right about the part I wanted to cut — not only was it necessary, it has become my favorite part of the book. Thank you for not listening to me. I didn't realize how trite my desires were, in all their specifics, until, after announcing my major some two years later, I found out that everyone else was thinking the same thoughts. My wish to render the world through words, delicately coloring the minutiae of daily life and skillfully tackling solipsism, was the same wish that every single person writing a story seemed to have, every single kid sending off an application to the Iowa Writer's Workshop had, every high-school sophomore connecting with Holden Caulfield had.

Intro creative-writing workshops at Columbia were very difficult to get into, perhaps because they're an easy enough class to get a good grade in, some innocent GPA-boosting. Or maybe people are just that interested in writing as a hobby. For whatever reason, it's nearly impossible for an incoming freshman to get into a workshop. I was extraordinarily lucky to make it in off the waitlist. It was a sign, I thought. I was meant to do this. I figured I was going to impress the students and make friends right away. But the makeup of the class was not what I had envisioned. These kids didn't seem to want to read and write like Hemingway, they wanted to curse and be Bukowski or write young adult fantasy. I moved forward toward my goal regardless.

The first story I ever submitted went over fine in class. It was my initiation into the obscure undergrad-writing-class etiquette in which I would eventually become fluent. The other students seemed perfectly unaffected by my story, responding to it only to the degree demanded by workshop decorum. Later, our professor, whose most recent book I had read before the semester and thought was pretty OK, asked each of us to meet with her after our first critique for one-on-one feedback. After all, we were beginners and she was an expert. She didn't have an office, so I met her in the Dodge classroom. I nervously anticipated the meeting.

Graham, I've got to say this story is really great. I'm really impressed with it, she told me.

I looked down at the table, humbled and embarrassed. I had made it.

I think once you edit this, you're going to have a really amazing piece. It's really close to being there already, but with some revisions it's going to be a perfect little nugget.

Thank you so much, I said.

I had no idea why I was so lucky, why my first story out of the gate was being praised so highly. I fully committed to writing at that moment. I had what it takes, I had the gift. Out of the however many thousands of people pursuing collegiate writing, I felt at that moment that I was going to be the one who wrote the book that people read. I just needed some revisions.

This momentum did not maintain. I would never get praise as high again. I worried that I was unable to hone my potential or that I had lost it entirely. Or maybe, save for that one professor's stroke of beginner's luck, no one was capable of realizing that I was special.

But, even in my most ignorant period, I knew my characters needed something beyond what I could give them. Some sort of roundness, maybe better put as a *realness*, that I couldn't put my finger on. My stories needed a certain touch that, as I repeatedly discovered, my hands were incapable of applying. I wanted to be a laconic Steinbeck, a more depressed Salinger, a Mid-Atlantic O'Connor. I wasn't. I was none of those, I was just a college student trying to understand the world through stories in real time. This all slowly chipped away at the statue of my writerly dream until, four years later, there was almost nothing left.

My parents continued not to pressure me as I, increasingly tired of feeling like a hack, brooded over whether to change my major. Regardless of the feedback I got, which consisted in the main of general pleasantries and bland reassurances, or the good grades I received (creative work can't be graded on merit, only effort — a big help for my GPA and the best argument for staying with the major), I felt that I was missing the mark, that I was doing a disservice to the craft. I started to pull in influences from my own life, writing characters directly lifted from my family, because what young adult truly has enough experience to write something interesting anyway? I wasn't an adventurer or a hero. I was a kid who showed up to class 10 minutes early and still didn't fully understand what was going on, still felt out of place and misunderstood and stupid, even though I was at one of the best schools, a kid from a loving family, and healthy, save for the occasional cold sore. So then there were a batch of stories about a Columbia creative-writing major trying to get their act together amid the difficulties of young adulthood: trying to figure out love, identity, and the meaning of young life. But, fearing that my family would disapprove of their fictional representations, I abandoned that, too. That was the end of my writing dream. That and the fact that every story I ever submitted to a journal, website, review, or magazine was swiftly turned down with a thank you for the submission and a "not the right fit for us." I was encountering clichés everywhere I turned:

the privileged yet sad teen, the misunderstood writer, the suburbanite fleeing to New York, and now the inevitable return. It was too late to change my major and I didn't want to start something new, so I just played out the string. Writing, I then justified to myself, was the ability to present a precise idea in well-formed, easy-to-understand sentences, a desirable competency in any hiree. It wasn't about stories and ideas anymore, it was about being understood. About understanding. I could work in marketing, publicity, teaching, maybe as a lawyer if I wanted to.

I scratch my arm. Creative writing, I say.

Oh wow, that's neat. Am I going to get one of your books at Barnes & Noble one day?

I laugh. No, no, I don't think so. I'm not going to be an author, it's just something I enjoy. I treated it more like an English degree — learning to write and communicate effectively. I've been applying for a bunch of jobs since I graduated, just sending out résumés and cover letters to whoever will take it. I'm actually hoping to hear back from some places soon.

My father lends a supporting nod, slowly rocking his head back and forth. I keep telling him he'll be just fine. Times are different now, you can have two or three careers in your life. You don't need to have it lined up right away. Everything will work out.

The bald-headed Korbel agrees. Yeah you're going to do great. Don't worry about it. A school like that and a bright kid like you, I'm sure you'll get a great job. It will all come together. Hell, we'll probably be working for you in five years! You'll be running the SBO, I bet! He pulls out his phone to check the clock. 9:56 a.m., he shows us. All right, me and your dad should head on up there, it's about time for this to start.

My father pats me on the shoulder as Korbel extricates his hand from the briefcase and offers it out, our hands meeting in the middle and embracing each other. I imagine his hand as offering encouragement and mine as offering some form of sympathy. I sit back down in my seat as they walk to the stage.

Vanek approaches the lectern set at the far end of the executive board table. He scoots by the icon, whose position, I realize now, is slightly too close to the table given the slimness of the stage. There's no way for him to face the delegation without turning sideways and sucking in his stomach behind board members' backs and the icon. He begins to speak through his voice box to remarkably little effect, his language close to inaudible and, for the majority of the audience, all but indecipherable. But here he is, our fearless leader, addressing the flock. He speaks slowly.

Dad: We now move on to the report of the bylaw committee. Legal Counsel Andrew Sojka will give us his report.

Sojka: Good morning.

All: Good morning.

Sojka: Motion by the Supreme Council that the bylaw committee recommends as follows: to amend Bylaw Section 108 as follows . . . has the Sergeant at Arms not handed the bylaws out? It should be in your packet. Section 108 should be the next to last page in your bylaws. It should be in red. Has everyone received a copy of the proposed amendment? (*Papers shuffle, folders open, and reports are removed.*) By motion of the Supreme Council, the bylaw recommends as follows to amend Bylaw Section 108 as follows: the Society shall record and report unclaimed property annually by April 15, as required by Pennsylvania's Disposition of Abandoned and Unclaimed Property Act, 72 PS, sections 1301.1-1301.29. I move that this motion be accepted. President Vanek accepts it. Any questions?

Dad: There's been a motion made by the Bylaw Committee and seconded by President Vanek. On the question, is there any discussion? Yes.

Michelle Vanek: I just wanna urge everyone to vote against this. Being a scholarship recipient myself, my sister and I benefited greatly from it. We have children ourselves now and we know that they will benefit greatly. And it just, we think, encourages other future members to join, knowing they could receive a scholarship. Who the heck wants to give that money to the state when we can continue keeping it in our organization?

Someone: Right! Right!

Dad: OK. I think we have another comment. Harold Vasko.

Vasko: Delegate . . . 42. I have a few things to say. My name's Harold Vasko, delegate 42. Our bylaws were written in 1913, which precedes the writing of this state law. We place about $25,000 each year from these unclaimed funds directly into the scholarship funds. I benefit from that, my family has benefited from that, many of us in this room have benefited from that. This bylaw will basically be a cut of $25,000 from that scholarship fund. We're the only fraternal in Pennsylvania that has been requested to comply with this. All the others place their unclaimed funds in their scholarship funds. So, because of all that — because of the discussion that we've heard already — I urge voting against this. Thanks.

(*Applause.*)

Dad: Thank you, thank you. Yes?

Bryan: Len Bryan, Lodge 215, delegate 63. I did a little research on this this morning, to the best of my ability. You do have to do a due diligence of paying this money to the beneficiaries.

Dad: Which we constantly do, every month.

Bryan: And there is a liminal period — I'm sure all the board members know about the liminal period — that we are required to hold money for three years. We're doing our part, so I vote this down. I say no.

Dad: Thank you, and just to comment further, and Lauren will attest to this, somebody shows up 15 years from now and they happen to be a beneficiary to that policy, we pay them.

Someone: You ain't gonna pay them if you don't have the money.

Dad: No, but we'll have the money.

Someone: No, but I'm saying . . .

Dad: Oh we won't have the money if the state has the money. No, you're right. Try to get it from them.

Someone: Exactly.

Dad: Thank you. Is there any other discussion on this

motion? Yes?

Abram: Stephen Abram, delegate 37. Does the organization have any choice in this matter? Doesn't the state law supersede certain bylaws?

Dad: We've sought legal counsel on this, from the Pennsylvania Fraternal Solicitor, and he indicates that because our bylaws precede the state law, that we are in good standing should this come to a head in court. We'd win this matter because we have a contract with our people when you buy a policy, that the state can't come in and change that contract. That would be our standing point. The other issue is, it's about $25,000 now, but that amount keeps shrinking because this only pertains to the real old policies where we've lost contact with people. Today you buy a policy, we have good contacts, and we try to keep in contact with people so they're updated. So as Lauren will attest, that amount keeps shrinking. It won't be $25,000 for much longer. The other thing is, as Harold brought up, we're the only fraternal that the state has tagged with this. And the others have not challenged yet because they haven't been tagged with it. Now, if they challenge us on this, then we have to decide what we're going to do. If we're going to challenge it in court or not. The last time we had a challenge to a footnote it took eight years before it was resolved. And if we can get eight more years out of this, we're probably going to be in real good shape because I don't think there will be many more unclaimed properties after eight years. Minimal, most likely. So yes, the state laws are there. But our bylaws are also there. I think that we're trying to show that. Does that answer your question sufficiently? That's a good point, though, because that's the whole issue right there. Anyone else? All right, I guess it's time for a vote. Voting in favor of amending the bylaws to give the state the money, say aye.

(*Silence.*)

Dad: Those opposed to amending the bylaws to give the state the money, say no.

All: No.

Dad: I say the nays have it and that amendment to the bylaws is defeated. Andrew, your first amendment to the bylaws has been defeated.

Sojka: I had one last time, don't worry. One and one.

Dad: Thank you. Now, this is very important, maybe the most important thing of the morning. Phil Hubik is going to explain your vouchers and how to fill them out. If you don't do the vouchers right, you don't get paid, so it's very important. So Phillip will explain the vouchers.

Lunch is in the restaurant of the hotel. The entirety of the Organization has convened down here to enjoy pre-made sandwiches and a selection of Wise chips. The same group separations have occurred and I am left circling tables aimlessly, looking for my family like an infant lost in the mall. I am all alone on the blue-tiled floor surrounded by the entire delegation of the Slavic Brotherhood Organization.

The sandwiches — various types of hoagie (Italian, turkey, roasted veggie, tuna salad) wrapped in that thick deli paper — are already out on silver platters, and people have formed a line to pick up their preferred choice. The sandwiches are cold. They are supposed to be, but that always seems strange to me. Why would you want a cold sandwich? I think I might skip lunch today.

My parents arrive at the restaurant. The Vice President and the Second Lady. For wielding such power in the Organization and for being such public figures, my parents walk in nonchalantly and unnoticed. The illusion exists that the powerful and the ordinary are the same and that they are all equal here, an egalitarian society. Especially at this convention. Because to be Russian Orthodox, or Serbian or Greek Orthodox or whatever, in America in the 21st century means that you exist in a culture — probably a subculture, more appropriately — where there are so few people that there should be no room for a hierarchy. And even that number is dwindling. You know everyone involved in the church in your town, probably the town over and, through functions like this, across the entire Rust Belt, which seems to be really the only place where the Orthodox church exists, as that's where most Slavic immigrants settled a hundred years ago. Awareness of this is paramount to the modern Orthodox experience, and as such it's an important component of the convention attendees' identity, as is a certain do-gooder Americanness rooted in severe distrust, or outright hatred, of communism, everyone here aware of the Motherland's anti-American ideology and its transgressions against our ancestors.

I was baptized in the Orthodox church, but I was never really a member of it. I don't think of myself as being Russian because I barely am. The Russo identity was extremely important to my father and his generation, though, I think.

His father helped rebuild the church in Wilkes-Barre, Holy Resurrection Orthodox Church on North Main Street, which is actually a pretty beautiful building that always reeks of incense. My paternal grandfather was even baptized by Alexis Toth, who would later be canonized, or glorified, as the Orthodox say, as St. Alexis of Wilkes-Barre, and whose relics are still in the church and whose likeness stands behind the Executive Board today. Alexis became the first pastor of Holy Resurrection after coming to America in the late 19th century, leaving the memory of a dead wife and child behind in Austria-Hungary. He arrived in Minneapolis as a Uniate but reported to a Catholic archbishop, who refused to recognize him as a priest, since doing so would have been contrary to the diocese's policy of Americanization and integration. After flirting with the idea of returning to Europe, Alexis decided to track down a Russian Orthodox bishop in San Francisco, and was eventually welcomed, along with his whole parish, into the Russian Orthodox church. This shift landed him in Wilkes-Barre, of all places, where he continued to spread Eastern Orthodox doctrine. To say he's an important figure for Mid-Atlantic Slavs, especially here in Wilkes-Barre, would be to say the least.

This Russian connection was lost in my generation. My family almost exclusively attended the Methodist church that my mother was a member of, the church that I was confirmed in as a pre-teen. We went to Holy Resurrection a few times a year growing up, usually on Orthodox holidays, which have familiar names but fall on unfamiliar dates, due to the Orthodox church recognizing the Gregorian calendar instead of the Julian one. So Russian Easter is sometimes as far as three weeks apart from normal Easter and Russian Christmas is celebrated on January 7th, which was fine by me — more presents that way. The annual trips to North Main Street were strange. Even at a young age, I felt voyeuristic, the culture of the church was so alien. The church itself was dark and vacant, making me feel as if I were being inducted into a secret society.

The Vaneks walk in behind my dad, Henry still perched over, his tight smile pulling himself forward, with Mrs. Vanek walking politely beside him. I have successfully avoided Vanek the whole day so far, all three waking hours of it. I know there's no way to avoid confrontation with him no matter how hard I try, because no matter how badly I want things to be normal, they just aren't at the moment.

I take a seat at the bar so my back is to the restaurant's entrance, to Vanek. A man with longer hair and five days' scruff sits next to me, sunglasses dangling precariously from the neck of his plain-black T-shirt.

Hey kid, how you doing? Nice to meet you. He extends hi hand. Name's Rick.

Hey, nice to meet you. I'm Graham.

Where you from, Graham?

Oh I'm from right here in Wilkes-Barre. Kingston, actually, right across the river.

That must be nice for you. Don't have to travel or anything. I had to take off an extra day of work just to travel here. Makes it so goddamned hard to make it out here. But at least I'm the driver of my clan, so I'm getting, what was it, 50 cents a mile? 54? Something like that right?

Yeah, I think it was 54, they said.

Lucky for me, he laughs. Making the big bucks driving out here.

Where are you from? I ask.

I'm from out in Ohio, a bunch of us here are from there. I'm out near Akron, in a town called Fairlawn.

I've heard of Akron.

Yep, that's where I'm from. Nice place, I like living there. But having to come all the way out here was rough. It's a six-hour drive, you know? I had to take Friday off to begin with and I had to take a half day on Thursday to be able to just make it here. It's nice I'm getting paid a little for this, but it's hard to just miss work like that.

What do you do for work?

I work in machine manufacturing. I work for a company that basically builds machines for other people to build stuff with. CNC machines, they're called, computerized machines basically. Computer numerical control, it stands for. So it's nothing special but it's a nice job, I like it. We do stuff for cars, plastic, construction.

No that sounds pretty interesting.

Thanks, kid. You're too nice. How about you? You in school yet?

I actually just finished. Graduated a couple months ago, back in May.

Well . . . congrats. Must be nice, got everything ahead of you still.

That's part of the problem. Too many choices to make, and I don't know what to do.

You seem like a smart kid, I'm sure you'll figure it out.

71

It's not worth getting worked up about. You'll get a job and you'll make it work, we all do. Just don't go into real estate or something, those guys are in hot water right now. I don't think it's as bad as they say it is out there. I never lost my job, I know a couple of guys who were fired, but everyone I know works in an industry where they need real guys to do the work and whatever. People are still doing work. Some of my friends have to go down to Cleveland, but I don't know anyone who just has been completely out of work for the last three years or anything.

Thanks, yeah. I hope so.

Trust me on that. Any idea what you want to do for a career?

Uh, I don't know yet, I've been applying for a lot of jobs. I've been trying to just get my foot in the door anywhere, but I studied writing, so I think the stuff I have the best shot at is copywriting or technical writing or something like that.

Oh, I don't know anything about that. But good luck.

Thanks, I appreciate it.

Rick unwraps his tuna hoagie and places the paper down on the plate. He has a thick plastic cup filled with Coke, one of those red ones you can barely see through.

You know I've been trying to come to this convention for years. I've been a member of the SBO for near a decade. We have the most active lodge in the whole Organization out in Ohio, almost as old as the SBO itself. We've got a really good group of people out there and we do a lot of great stuff. You know Phil Hubik, right? The Secretary Treasurer? He's the head of our lodge, good friend of mine. Anyway, we do a big fundraiser every summer to raise money for the scholarship fund, we have nice dinners and stuff, we have great pierogis and halusky, we have monthly meetings. And I've been trying to come out to a convention because I really care about the SBO. I'm out there pushing it on my friends and coworkers. I'm out there making sure that our dinners are well attended so we can make a little money for our parish and help people get involved. Help people know that they can get money for their kids for school and a life-insurance policy — you know, the same spiel they've been giving us here so far. I want to see it do well. But I'll tell you what, they sure don't make it easy for us to help them. I'm missing out on making money at work to be here. I had to take off a day and a half just to be here, Thursday just for driving, too. And it's all right because I want to be here, but I could use those vacation days for something with my family. That's one thing you realize when you get a job, the vacation days are precious. They're the most important part about the job, almost. You need to be able to get away, unwind, and decompress. And it's not just good to be able to do that, it's necessary. That's one piece of advice I've got for you in your job search: don't forget that work is work. Make sure you get paid, make sure you get what you deserve, but make sure that you don't forget that it's supposed to help you get to where you need to go. The money and the work and everything are all supposed to help you enjoy your life in other ways. So that's why you get the nice TV or go on a nice vacation, because you earned it. You deserve it. You gotta be able to do what you want, if only sometimes.

I sit there, still. Rick grabs the left half of his hoagie off the checkered wrapping paper and lifts it to his mouth, taking a bite with no remorse.

With his mouth still full, Rick starts talking again. So, yeah, you just make sure that you can do what you want. And being here to help the SBO, that's what I want. So it's a pain that I won't be able to spend two extra days at the lake, that's definitely true, but there are other things that are important on a personal level as well. This is what I got from my dad. Being a member of the church, caring about making sure that it lasts, you know. So I do both. This is like work, too, because it requires me showing up and putting in my energy, but this is what fulfills me. And so it might not be relaxing, but it's rewarding.

I get what you mean.

Ha, good, kid.

There is a certain level of information that I took for granted that only now becomes apparent to me. Yes, there are 60-some people here, I knew that, but some of these people actually want to be here. Some of these people make certain sacrifices just to be able to hear reports read to them, reports that can be emailed or condensed to a very short list of bullet points. They think that this, the SBO, is necessary and should be strengthened, maintained, and cared for.

And then there's me.

I don't even know what lodge I belong to. I've never been to a meeting. I've never been to an SBO dinner. I've never sold a life-insurance policy. I don't even know that I have one, really. I just come to the conventions and now get paid $600 to sit here and watch people try to save an organization that is destined to fail. One that has no business being a business. I'm here because my father asked me to be and wanted to give me money. Free money, he told me. Come to the convention and you'll get $600 just for sitting there. My mom gets even more than me for checking people in and she doesn't even sit in on the meetings. No one needs to sit in on the meetings. No one at all. The delegates' presence here does not offer anything other than a voting body for measures that will surely pass without them.

It feels like there's a wrongly accepted inevitability: that the Slavic Brotherhood Organization must continue to exist.

One of the most important things that I learned through my creative writing degree was that we crave an unrealistic idea of reality. We tell ourselves about our lives in a narrative fashion and we think of our lives in the same way off the page. But life is not lived in a narrative. The narrative is a lie passed down to us, generation after generation. Our lives are not A to B to C all the way to death at Z. It would be nice if it were so clean and easy, if cause led to effect and the chain built itself and were easily identifiable. At some point, literature in the West began to go out of its way to reject A-B-C cleanliness. The stream of consciousness of Joyce or Woolf was supposed to be a more realistic representation of the way that humans actually operate. That, too, was another lie, but it was so formally innovative and exciting that a certain class of educated people came to believe that humans really do think like that and act like that and that life goes on like that. Later, Raymond Carver and all the MFA-ites focused on another new realism, that of unimportant, daily life, another twist and still another lie. I thought it was true as true could be. A gold standard, a shining light. I didn't realize the ways in which it was not true until the end of my college career, as I watched myself unpack boxes and twiddle my thumbs in my childhood bedroom. All these writers, irrespective of whatever aesthetic movement or counter-movement they were associated with, had been trying to show the progression of life, the arc. I was supposed to be in the next step, I was supposed to be smarter and better adjusted to the world and to be starting on the next chapter of my life: career. Which really is shorthand for adulthood. Everything else has been a training exercise. First we learn how to obey rules, then we learn how to problem-solve, then we learn how to balance multiple tasks at once while going through whatever personal problems adolescence brings, then learn critical thinking, and then and only then do we pay our own taxes. All these skills are built off one another. It's like learning a language. You start with the foundation, the present tense and simple declarations, and then you practice that until you're ready to move onto more complicated situations, past and future tense, and then you further complicate it by adding concepts that make language truly personal, conditionals and expressions of doubt. My fluency in adulthood, though — my ability to shop for myself and do my laundry, separating my lights from my darks and adding the right amount of fabric softener — led not to a new place but to the same place I was in high school. It was a loop.

And so here I am, the same person I was four years ago. Whereas before I was innocent and on a trial run of adulthood, running clubs and extracurricular as if they were my hobbies and school as if it were my job, I was now in a crash course of what it really was. And I opt out. This can't be my arc. It must not exist, or maybe it skipped me over. So now I must take some action. If things aren't happening for me, I have to make them happen myself. If I don't like the picture, I'll just make my own.

Rick takes another bite out of his sandwich. Hey, here comes Vanek, he says out of the side of his mouth.

Henry Vanek stands behind, smiles his mute smile and waves. He appeared with almost no introduction, as in a horror movie with no soundtrack and no blood, just the threat of confrontation.

Rick starts speaking, unafraid of Vanek's power.

Hi, Henry, how you doing? Great to meet you. My name is Rick. Rick Zhukovsky. I'm from Lodge 204 in Akron. I'm really truly honored to be here at the Supreme Convention. I've been a member for many years and have always been so proud of the Organization and am happy that I'm finally able to come and help move us forward. You've done a great job and I'm happy to help out in any way that I can.

Vanek puts out his palms, pumping the breaks. He shakes his head. Vanek does a great job of acting like he has nothing to do with the Organization, a public modesty that translates well to constituents. There is no credit taken. As if all honor is to the Organization, not to Vanek. The SBO is the cause and the creator, and Vanek, like all of us, can only respect it and oil its gears.

Well it's great to be here. I'm really happy I could make it.

Rick's criticisms, valid ones at that, are now completely

lost. It's as if he is star-struck. Vanek turns to me.

Hi, Mr. Vanek, how are you doing today? I ask.

He nods, continuing his smile. He extends his right forearm over his stomach, pointing one finger to his left, thrusting it back and forth into space. I follow his motion and realize he is pointing toward the emptiness at the end of the bar. Follow me, his finger says. The open seats have an ominousness to them, knowing our presence is intended.

You want to head over there? I ask.

He nods again.

Rick extends his hand to shake, and Vanek accepts. Vanek bows his head in deep gratitude and Rick smiles warmly. Vanek proceeds to the end of the bar, which is completely vacant despite being in the middle of the crowded room. I have to get up and follow. The noise from the crowd is loud. People are laughing and talking and catching up again. Vanek and I hide in plain sight, the Hubiks sitting within a few tables, oblivious. I catch Ollie looking at me as I make my way down the bar. I smile at her and she smiles back, but the moment is too stressful for me to indulge in my fantasy life with her. My hands are at my side but I flip my fingers up in a gentle, somber wave. Her arms are crossed on the table, one over the other, with each hand resting on its opposite elbow. She lifts four fingers off the elbow leaving her thumb as an anchor, extending the same weak greeting that I gave her. No one notices us.

Vanek puts his pad of paper down on the bar before sitting.

HAVE U THOUGHT ABOUT MY OFFER?

Yes, yes. I thought about it a little but I haven't had much time.

WE ONLY HAVE 1 MORE DAY. I NEED YOUR DECISION ASAP

I don't get it, Mr. Vanek. I'm not a good candidate for this job, I don't know anything about its qualifications or its duties. I just need a job is all, otherwise I wouldn't be interested. I don't want to make an enemy. This is just a big decision, I'm sorry. I need just a little more time. Please.

ITS NOT A BIG DECISION. YOU WANT THE JOB OR YOU DONT. ITS SIMPLE

Vanek is lying. It is neither simple nor small. It isn't just taking a job or not; it's whether I want to be party to intentionally hurting someone, even if it's not my hurt to give. But what am I supposed to do? If I don't do it, someone else will. And it's not that I can't keep sending out résumés and cover letters. I could still get a real job somewhere else, and this would give me a real line item on my résumé. A new set of skills to embellish. New references. This could help start something for me.

When do you need to know by? I ask Vanek, replacing my worried and childish tone with that of a mature and certain adult.

ASAP . . . he writes

I stare around the room again, seeing only a handful of people I recognize. This is not my Organization. These are not my people. This is my future, though, and I need to take control of it.

OK, I'll do it.

Henry stares at me blankly.

I'll do it, I'll do it.

He breaks into a smile and extends his bony wrinkled hand. We shake over the Formica bar. Vanek leans in and through his computerized voice he says thank you into my ear. The computer voice only speaks at one volume, he cannot whisper.

Dad: OK, thank you, I think everyone has a copy of the President's Report, and we're now under that section for the good of the order, and President Vanek has prepared a report to show you some of the growth that we have done in the last, uh, nine years. And if you look — where we are, where we were, and what we need to do. So the first thing you see is our surplus: so in 2004 it was $2,500,000, and last year it was $2,850,000, so that's a nice number and it grew. Obviously not by a lot, but the environment has been a bit tumultuous, as we all know. Our assets: in 2002 we were $10 million, last year we were $14,600,000. As I said, we're approaching $15 million, so that's a nice growth, thanks in part to selling the old office. Our solvency ratio, which is something that Rob Moore figures out for us, as you will hear from him a little later — uh, in 2009 it was 127.5 per cent, and now we've increased to 129.8 per cent — an enviable percentage. All the other fraternals have their tongues hanging out at us because we have such a great solvency. In 2004 we lost $104,000 from our operations, and in 2012 we gained $104,000 in operations, that's like a $208,000 reversal. Our total expenses in 2004 were $501,000, and in 2011 they decreased to $484,000 despite inflation. The face amount of insurance, 2008 was $4,800, and now it's $5,300. The surplus change in 2004 was a $1,187,000 loss, and in 2012 a $108,000 gain. Flip it over. Life insurance: in 2004, membership, we had 3,475 members. Now we have 3,298 members. *This is our big problem.* That's what they're trying to address here. We cannot continue to exist if membership continues to drop. Even though our financial numbers are good, we need members. We need members *desperately.* We're going to have a big membership drive later, we want you to go out and be soldiers for us and sell policies, sell annuities, make presentations to your church, to your friends — everyone you meet who has a baby, try to sell them a policy. It's great. It's an easy sell. We have the lowest rates around. We have the best benefits around! People just have to know about us. And then you also heard that our online website is starting to get results, thankfully. We got our one policy in the bank and one on the way, and that hopefully is just going to continue to increase. But if there's anything to this convention, we need to sell policies. And Lauren will haunt you in your sleep unless you sell policies! So that is a definite. Everyone should buy or sell at least one policy. Even if you feel you don't need insurance or no one in your family needs insurance, everyone can use an annuity. It's like putting $100 in the bank. And we pay 3 per cent, which no bank will give you. And when you need it, you call us, and we send you the money! How easy can it be? It's like more savings. And if you continue to add $100 every so often, you'll see how that builds. And it's tax-sheltered, you're not paying tax on it. Our goal, hopefully, is to sell 100 new policies at this convention. And you heard the incentive for an insurance policy, it's $50 — there's no incentive for an annuity because it's basically putting money in the bank, but it still adds to our members and we have to show an increase in our members. If we keep losing members, we may have to merge with another society. And this is something we keep hearing, we keep pondering. I wonder if that footnote from the state on our audit is a nudge to say, Hey, you better do something. We don't want to merge. We're financially solvent, but the only way we can show the state we're doing something is to get new members. They're on us now, what are we doing to get new members? We have to show an increase in membership. Let's all agree to sell at least one policy a year for the next four years so at our next convention we can show a growth. We would love to present this same report in four years and show a growth in membership. We have to do it if we're going to continue to exist. Henry says get a friend at work or a relative to buy a $100 annuity. I mean that's the easiest sell there is, $100 annuity. It's like taking $100 and putting it away for a rainy day. And we should all do that at some point, if you haven't done it already. And it's a great retirement tool — it's tax-sheltered, it's tax-free. So please consider that. Please, yourselves, consider it here. When you go home, next Sunday when you're in church, when you're visiting people, start thinking who can buy a policy. Again, it is an easy sell. Remember, it's the best insurance around. And we don't sell million-dollar policies, we don't sell half-million-dollar policies. The highest policy that we sell is $50,000. What we're gearing towards now is burial insurance, enough money to cover your funeral. We're not selling money to cover or protect your family if you're a young person. But every funeral now costs around $10,000 ,and that's the selling point, for someone to cover your funeral.

Now, we're slightly ahead of schedule so, good news everyone, we're going to get you out even earlier than anticipated. But please keep in mind everything we're talking about. We've got a block of time dedicated to discussing new ideas later on, so please everyone put on your thinking caps and hopefully together we can start to solve this. OK everyone, enjoy your break.

The Friday dinner is the same process as lunch, an informal affair in the hotel bar, more buffet food: pasta, steamed vegetables, mashed potatoes, a carving station manned by a chef with a large straight white hat. I don't want to go but I don't have anything else going on and I hope that I can talk to Ollie some more at the dinner. I'm thinking about her still and how our being together is an absurd idea. It doesn't make any sense. But that's not how these things work — you have to follow your intuition, you have to try things. This is, after all, the reclamation of my arc. But Ollie won't want to see me if she thinks I'm taking revenge on her father. I have already created a story; my degree is being put to good work. This is why I studied writing, maybe, to help me write my life the way I want, to write myself out of the bits that could implicate me.

Vanek's plan was enacted against my will, I'll tell her. I had no choice in the matter. I am bound to show up to the voting Sunday morning, tied into a plot without my consent. Owning up to the plan is against the rules. Vanek threatened my father's job, I'll say. The SBO isn't the mob, I know. The name certainly sounds like it, but it's not. No one dies other than from old age and cancer, and when they do the SBO pays out. That's their business plan. But I can't betray my father, I can't have my errors be his downfall. Vanek's revenge plot is his own and he wants it that way and I will keep it that way. Revenge is not my plan, simply employment.

I see Ollie standing at the bar drinking a Coke and I approach her, smiling, and say hi. She's standing in a line with her parents, Rick from lunch, and other various SBO members I don't recognize. They're all talking and Ollie is just staring on. She's wearing a different shirt, a red, black, and white blouse, short-sleeved and summery. She looks nice.

Hi, she says back.

Hello, Graham, her mother says, turning around to greet me.

Phil Hubik nods.

Nice convention, isn't it? I ask.

Oh it is, it is, Jane says.

Your dad's doing a great job, he's running the whole show, isn't he? Phil asks.

Yeah, he always is. He's got the voice for it.

Phil smirks, and leans the opposite direction. The conversation halfway down the line continues, Rick telling some joke and Phil listening in.

Are you trying to eat dinner here?

I mean, I don't think I have any other options.

Would you be interested in getting pizza? There's a really great pizza place not too far from here. It's a place called Angelo's, it's my favorite pizza. Better than anything I had in all of New York. Seriously. I've got my car right out back here.

Ollie smiles and bites her bottom lip.

Um . . . I would like to, but . . . hold on one second.

She turns to her parents. They have also changed outfits and stand there in their Friday-night attire, looking content and cool-headed, cultivating the very image of SBO royalty, executive board members not knowing their end is nigh. They're not getting whacked, he's just getting removed from a part-time vanity post, a $13k-a-year small-potatoes sinecure. Happens every day, it's OK, I tell myself. My cold sore tingles.

I see Phil and Jane Hubik look at me and feign smiles. Neither smile is their daughter's, theirs are dishonest and untrusting — I can't fault them — but they know me to be of a royal SBO bloodline as well. Ollie stands smiling and her father pats her on the back and her mother hugs her at her waist, approval having been granted.

That's no problem, my car's right through here, I say, leading the way.

We walk through the hotel quickly, passing over the monotonous, monochromatic palette draped around the entire building. I hold the glass door open for her as she walks in front of me into the July night. The Subaru's headlights blink as I unlock it walking up. I turn the ignition over and plug my phone into the cassette adapter, thinking quickly of what soundtrack to play. I put on Beach House's *Bloom* and turn down the volume some, the green LCD numbers on the console descending in attestation of my subtly considerate gesture.

So you've never been to Wilkes-Barre before, right? I ask.

No this is my first time. It's nice here, though. Do you like it?

Yeah, yeah, of course I do. It's complicated but I do. It's a nice place, though. I'll show you around quick.

I take a left on Market Street towards Public Square, trying to keep my pace normal and welcoming.

This is supposed to be downtown Wilkes-Barre. Not much of a downtown, though, as you can see. There's not really a center of business or anything anywhere here. There hasn't been a real industry here since the coal mines shut down. This up here on the left is the Kirby Center, which is a nice old theater, I say pointing out my window. The lights under the awning of the Kirby, hundreds of orange-glowing bulbs, light up the sidewalk. And this is Public Square. The tour was quickly ending as there wasn't much to show and I had even less to say. My relationships to these places amounted to having driven by them year after year.

This looks very pretty at night.

Hey you don't have to lie to me. I know it's not, it's OK. We laugh.

Come on, don't talk about where you're from like that! It's a nice place. Really. I like it.

I know, I know. I just am driving by all these places and realizing that I don't have much to say about it. I feel like I don't even know it that well myself.

That's OK.

You know what, I've been a real jerk. I've barely asked you about yourself at all. I haven't even asked you about your school or your major or anything. I'm sorry, I'm not usually this selfish, I don't think.

We've barely talked this weekend, don't worry about it. But since you're asking, I'm at Pitt and I'm doing biology.

Biology, wow, that's pretty cool. And Pitt's a great school, too. You're close to home there, right?

Yeah I'm only about an hour and a half from my parents'. It's nice to have some distance but still be able to go home when I want, do laundry for free and whatever. Get a home-cooked meal. You know. And biology's not really that cool when it's all you do, but I still enjoy it at times, so thank you.

I just imagine that it's nice to have a right and wrong answer. You either are correct or you're incorrect. I would've loved that.

I mean people are doing experiments, our understanding of biology changes with the more information that we get and everything. For instance, I'm really studying ecology and evolution, human evolution. How we got to be where we are. The time we're covering in that field is so vast because it goes back almost 100 million years and the changes don't just occur instantaneously. So someone will make a discovery and claim they've found an ancestor or, you know, a missing link, for lack of a better term, and they'll claim it confirms a certain idea of evolution and others will argue against it. That's making it really simple, but you get what I'm saying. So we don't really have answers — we have a lot of complicated questions, and there are schools of thought that you can subscribe to, but there's not a true right and wrong with that.

I smile.

What!

Oh no, nothing. Sorry. I like hearing you talk about it. I like hearing you say "we." You're in the group of experts, you're in the crew.

Ha! I don't mean it like that, like I'm an expert. I'm still just a student.

No I get it, it's just nice. That's just not something I ever did in creative writing. You don't ever become an expert, it feels like. There's no "we" in writing, just a lot of "I." "We" like the first-person, I say mockingly. As we drive around the Square, the streetlights pass over the car, casting and dissolving shadows on Ollie's and my face.

I just imagine it must feel nice to be a part of something.

Yeah I'm not sure I feel a part of it yet, but I guess as I go on it will continue to feel more natural. More a part and less apart.

Sorry?

More a part, two words, and less apart, one word.

I laugh. That's clever. You should be a writer.

She smiles. Thanks.

So this is River Street we're coming up on. This right up here on the right, behind this empty lot, this was actually this hotel called Hotel Sterling. They're supposed to tear it down next week. As you can tell, there's not much of a skyline or anything, but that building was always the kind of silhouette you'd recognize. It's like the river, the eagles up on pillars of the bridge there, and this little short building with its sign all falling apart — that's Wilkes-Barre. It's kind of sad.

Why are they going to tear it down?

Well it hasn't been open or anything since the '70s, I don't think. It's just been dilapidated. It used to be this really upscale hotel. Like my mom told me she and her family would get dressed up and come down to Wilkes-Barre on the weekends and just kind of walk around. She grew up 30 minutes away, kind of out in the sticks. That's what kind of place this town used to be. The Sterling was really the center of that. The light turns green and we take a left on River. And then in 1972, Wilkes-Barre got hit by Hurricane Agnes and the building flooded. That's like the history of this whole town: everything was going pretty well and then we got flooded and never bounced back. My house, which is probably a mile away from the river, got almost a foot of water on the first floor, so I can only imagine how bad the Sterling got it. But it closed down and never reopened, I don't think. I mean, it was never open in my life, at least, I know that. I'm not entirely sure on the history. The flood is basically the most important moment in the town's history, it kind of ruined everything. A lot of those buildings that are boarded up downtown were shut down in '72 and have just stayed that way ever since. But some company bought the Sterling trying to renovate it and bring it back a few years ago, and just ended up blowing all their money. They thought they could save the hotel, but it just turned into a money pit. Then the city had to bail them out. They put up $1 million to demolish the building, but it's taken years for it to actually get the demolition started. It's just sat here as long as I can remember, completely vacant and boarded up. I thought it'd always stay that way. Kids would break in for fun. My friends and I from high school always said we were going to get in there just to see what it was like. I guess I'll never get the chance now.

It's still there now. Why don't we go in?

What about the pizza? It's really good, I swear. They have this thing called sweet sauce —

She cuts me off. We can get pizza after, or any other time. They're tearing that building down, it's never coming back!

It's dark and everything . . . I honestly don't think it's a good idea to go now. I think homeless people stay in there at night. I don't even have a flashlight or anything. And you're wearing open-toed shoes!

OK that's the only reasonable point you've made. But let's go tomorrow or something.

You really want to go that bad?

Yes!

OK we'll go tomorrow. During lunch so it's light out?

It's a date.

SATURDAY

Bridgemen: On July 19, 2013, the meeting was called to order at 10 a.m. by President Henry Vanek, opening remarks were presented by Henry Vanek, invocation by Father Dubinsky, a moment of silence for departed members and family members led by Father Dubinsky, Pledge of Allegiance led by Michael S. Koval, procedurals given by Sergei Mercy. Naming of temporary chair held by Sergei Mercy, movement for temporary chair and secretary made by Sergei Mercy, roll call of officers made by Phillip Hubik, report of credentials committee made by Michelle Vanek, Chairman, naming there were 66 delegates present, Sergei Mercy declared a quorum present, designation of salaries for convention officers and stipends for committees was made by Martin M. Koval, proposed resolution, motion to accept proposed resolution made by Michael S. Koval, motion seconded by Theresa Koval, motion passed. Committee appointments listed by Thomas Wincheski and then promoted by Sergei Mercy. Thomas Wincheski, Chairmen of Nominating Committee, placed the name of Sergei Mercy for Convention Chairman, nomination from the floor none, motion to accept unanimously made by Carl Pasic, seconded by Martha Mungers. Motion carried. Thomas Wincheski, Chairmen of Nominating Committee, placed the name of Lauren Bridgemen and Melody Bartos for Convention Secretaries, nomination from the floor none, motion to accept unanimously made by Hazel Coates, seconded by Chris Shupanski. Motion carried. Opening remarks given by Sergei Mercy: the Pennsylvania State Audit has requested that there be a change in the bylaws to give unclaimed money to the state. We will vote on that later. SBO on selling the building on Spring Garden Street for $2 million plus, more than the appraised value. The new office in Chalfont is more modern. The SBO created a new website and other modern features to help increase membership. One policy has already been sold through the new website. Officer reports were given out at registration. Report and discussion of society business given by Lauren Bridgemen. Sergeant at Arms distributed copies of SBO bylaws, article 18, on Pennsylvania death benefits, that Pennsylvania asked us to change regarding unclaimed death benefits for SBO bylaw, to be discussed. Andrew Sojka indicated that the Supreme Council made the motion to accept the proposed change to the bylaws regarding the unclaimed property owned by the SBO. Therefore, the bylaws committee recommendation reads as follows: the society shall record and report unpaid property annually by April 16, as required by Pennsylvania state law. Motion to accept made by Andrew Sojka. Seconded by Henry Vanek. Discussion follows. "All in favor, all opposed, the nays have it." Vouchers were then discussed by Phillip Hubik. Status report where we discuss the business of the good of the Organization attached. Sergei Mercy read the report and discussed the information provided. "We cannot exist without members. SBO has the lowest rates and the best benefits. Sell policies." Sergei went over the schedule for activities for the night, then Sergei Mercy made a motion to adjourn for lunch until 1:30 p.m. Plenary Session Two was called to order by Matthew Korbel at 1:30. The membership drive was discussed by Matthew Korbel. The drive will run until the end of the convention, as an incentive all policies sold during the convention will receive an additional $50. Martin M. Koval discussed the scholarship drive, donation envelopes were provided in your totes. From the floor we received $3,065. Sergei Mercy went over the agenda for the rest of the evening. A closing prayer was held by Father Dubinsky and the meeting was adjourned at 3:45.

Dad: We all heard the minutes. Are there any additions or corrections to the minutes?

Vasko: I make a motion to accept the minutes as read. Harold Vasko, delegate 42.

Dad: Thank you, is there a second?

Zhukovsky: My name is Rick Zhukovsky, Lodge 204, delegate 52. I second.

Dad: Thank you, motion has been seconded. All those in favor?

All: Aye.

Dad: Rejected. Rather, against?

(*Silence.*)

The breakfast buffet is exactly the same as yesterday's, and that unshakable Groundhog Day feeling starts to set in. Routine makes everything feel safe. Waking up and being in the same place time and time again, doing the same thing over and over again, going to the same places incessantly. When you find this regularity, really sink into it, and are able to act without having to think about anything, time seems to speed up. When the schedule is broken, when you think about or notice it, time takes forever. My first semester at Columbia was an eternity. I was confused — I had thought I was accustomed to a school schedule. We are groomed on a Monday-to-Friday schedule as children, accepting the necessity, or at least the inevitability, of getting up early against our will and shuttling off to school. College was different. There was more autonomy in my daily life and a consequent adjustment period that I hadn't accounted for. In later years, time reverted to its normal pace as I recovered my routine: you have a task, you try to complete it, something gets in the way, you get stressed out, you go home, come back later, and you're eventually able to finish it after learning how incompetent everyone else around you is.

Nearly every person I've ever spoken to has told me how they're the only competent person they know. School project, work, anything — only one person seems to know how to do it the right way. Everyone else is just wrong and incredibly stupid, so stupid that it's amazing that no one else realizes just how dumb everyone else is, or questions how they were ever accepted into school or how they're not fired yet. Talk to someone long enough about other people and eventually they'll tell you that anything anyone else does is bound to be an exercise in extravagant ineptitude. It's the inverse of every parent believing their child is gifted: somehow every baby on Earth exhibits extraordinary cognitive functions on an accelerated timeline. Such exceptionalism would appear to bespeak an unashamed belief in self. I wouldn't know — my insecurities have always led me to believe that I am the fool compared to whom everyone feels so exceptional. It was hard not to see this confirmed in the futility of my job search prior to yesterday.

As for the weekend convention, with its extended speeches on protocol and finances, I'm once again in a pre-routinized state of confusion, in the throes of which I perceive time as having, sure enough, slowed down. Add to this the nerves and apprehension surrounding my new job, not to mention Ollie. My cold sore has, of course, not subsided. It's only gotten worse a mere one day into its lifespan — redder and crustier, occupying more space on my lip than before, expanding the frontier of its conquered territory almost to my nose. I can feel it just sitting there growing even when I'm not looking, its periodic tingles keeping me abreast of its movements.

Everyone has new clothes on today but looks the same as yesterday. I make a plate, covering the cold white ceramic with a mess of mostly tan foods, and sit with my parents, who are, at the moment, by themselves.

Hey kiddo, my mom says, a name she doesn't often call me.

Hey bud, my dad says.

Hi. How was last night? The bar do OK?

Oh yeah, my dad says. The room got shut down at around 11 or so, and Stinton wheeled that little soda-can-shaped cooler up to his room and tried to keep the party going. They got a call after being there for only 30 minutes to knock it off. It was those Pittsburgh guys, I think, just being loud and drunk. It's like they're college kids or something. But they're just having a good time. Can't knock 'em for that.

We laugh.

No you can't.

So I saw you talking with Ollie yesterday, my mom says. How's that?

It's fine, it's nothing really, I say, looking down at my plate.

She's cute, nice girl. I know Vanek's still pissed at her father from last convention but I think they're a nice family.

Yeah she's cute. We got Angelo's last night.

Angelo's! Graham, you can't take a nice girl like that to Angelo's. There's barely any place to sit down in there.

What? I think it's an accurate representation of our town.

My dad lets a small laugh out of the side of his mouth.

The morning proceedings are dry, like yesterday's. Motions are approved and things are explained that seem neither important nor understandable. At least to me. I can't help but feel bored to death. I sit in the back of the room and sink deeper in the rolly chair with each passing second. Every 30 minutes or so I have to hoist myself back up to a decorously upright position, my head having sunk to a level barely above the table and almost below my elbows, which are still propped up on the chair's arms. My body recurrently assumes a gelatinous state, my bones slowly disintegrating over the course of each 30-minute increment until I make a corrective movement that brings them back to life. The scent of breakfast lingers in the room and my mind wanders.

Having been back in Wilkes-Barre for a few months now, it's hard to make sense of my time away. I returned home seeing myself as equal parts changed and the same. At first, I tried to believe my return was triumphant, the golden son deigning to revisit humble beginnings. I had intellectually conquered Columbia, in as much as I completed a degree — really the bare minimum — and was now back where I had started for what was supposed to be a short break. This was my earned vacation, a bachelor party for my adolescence. That's what I told myself. It was taking longer than planned, so that what had seemed like just cause for exultation gradually revealed itself to be the step backward that it had always been.

The relationship between Columbia and Wilkes-Barre changed throughout my career. On the first few trips home, it was hard not to feel like I was *better* than when — and where — I had left. As if I had outgrown the old place. Of course, that didn't last. I had known before moving to New York that merely getting into a school with a low acceptance rate didn't make me better. The acceptance rate is a simple function of supply and demand: the school attracts many more applicants, owing mainly to name recognition, than it can accommodate. Acceptance doesn't make you smart any more than rejection makes you dumb. That's simple. But not simple enough for an 18-year-old to grasp.

The thing about coming to a place like Columbia is that as much as I wanted to fit in, I also wanted to be impressed. I wanted to feel second best. Put down. Dirt rubbed in my face. Exposed as the imposter I believed myself to be. Confirmed in my belief that the other students —the well-dressed, beautiful people from so many exotic and wonderful places, far more wonderful than Wilkes-Barre, at least — were geniuses. They were the real ones, the ones who knew what they were talking about. Knew what they wanted to be. Knew who they already were.

Some people tried to act like being there wasn't a big deal. That was genuine in some cases, I'm sure. There were also some people whose acceptance actually seemed to have been a mistake. It's true: some people were dumb. Not dumb as in not intelligent; dumb as in stupid. I saw people blatantly cheating on exams, not even attempting to hide their sideways glances. An expellable offense. Did they even want to be there? They probably had better things to do than memorize irregular conjugation for French II. I didn't.

Apart from these wanton displays of recklessness, though, there were more than enough reminders of my inadequacy to satisfy my desire for subordination. One time, early on in my freshman year, on a warm September day, the particular time of year when the students lie out on the steps of Low Library, enduring the roughness of the ground for a chance to enjoy a fleeting moment between the retreat of summer humidity and the onset of bitter, protracted winter cold, I was leaving class attempting to speak to a guy I thought could maybe be my friend. I was pitching myself, like a date or a job interview. It was a creative-writing class and he had made a reference to Borges, whose work, at the time, was one of my secrets. I was the biggest Borges fan I knew. I had maybe read two of his stories, impressive only by the standards of high-school students from Wilkes-Barre. Regardless, I liked and was inspired by his writing, though it, like so much else, has since come to taunt me. We talked for a few minutes while walking down the steps of Kent Hall before we had to go our separate ways. He was going somewhere that I wasn't, but I was hoping to continue talking to him at another time, to make a friend. I'm going to the cafeteria to eat, to Ferris, I said.

Cafeteria! he laughed. You mean dining hall?

I was embarrassed. I had missed noticing the point at which the place where you get food went from being the cafeteria to being the dining hall. Here, really, was the world-class education that I came to New York for. I never recovered from that interaction, and our relationship settled into a tortured weekly ritual of obligation-observance: we would make an unconvincing show of greeting each other before class and leave it at that.

Upon returning to a place where cafeterias are still cafeterias, I realized that my attempts to assimilate to Columbia's culture had perhaps been doomed from the start. I was too much a citizen of Wilkes-Barre. People move to New York all the time, but they are ready to live there and ready to leave their old life behind. Maybe their old life didn't make much sense to them. Mine was too much a part of me. In one of my earlier creative-writing classes, my professor always talked about his kid. He would share pictures and videos of his daughter in her highchair eating Cheerios and laughing, precious moments of youth caught candidly on his cellphone camera. As the semester kept going, he would share more, as if the relationship with the class were intensifying (I guess it was). Our last class ended with all of us sitting in a bar across Broadway, talking about life. You know how much they pay an adjunct lecturer at Columbia? he asked us rhetorically. $6,000 a semester. And they make it so you can only teach one class at a time. That's barely enough to live off of. We made gestures of commiseration, teens and early-20-somethings trying to sympathize with problems that we could not yet understand. He went on: I had to ask my dad for rent money the other month because I couldn't ask my wife. Do you know how embarrassing that is? I'm an adult, a published author with a PhD, and I had to go to my dad for rent money. For some reason, this man's abjectness cemented rather than shook my pledge to writing. He was from somewhere in Missouri, a suburb of St. Louis, I think. But these lessons he was learning in life and economics were New York problems. (Or maybe writerly problems. But, then, writerly problems tend to be downstream from New York problems.) He didn't leave New York. I gathered that he never even considered it. My daughter learns more about life spending one day at the playground than I did in six months in Missouri, he said once. I don't doubt that.

But the experiences he described — the hardships brought on by the toughness of the city, yielding wisdom you can't get any other way — were voluntary. That doesn't mean his struggle wasn't real; but it came, as it were, with the territory. Whereas most of New York's population comes to live there on an involuntary basis, born into it, those who decide to move to the city for all it might offer know full well what it will likely take in return. My professor's daughter is one of the former group, whose initial understanding of the world arises out of noise and traffic and subway delays and a very finite amount of space. Still, I believe what my professor said to be true: New York teaches more than other places to those who merely exist there. In my capacity as Columbia undergrad, however, I wasn't really learning New York. I was only learning Morningside Heights, an area with a lie for a name, an attempt to separate itself from its Harlem surroundings. The Columbia community often spoke of the "bubble," the imaginary space set up around campus that students refused to leave. It stretched from Absolute Bagels on 108th to the north end of campus on 120th: 12 blocks between Broadway and Amsterdam, and not much else. There was basically everything you needed there to survive, though that's never enough. As I became acclimated to the bubble, able to navigate and orient myself comfortably and easily, the wall I had built up, and upon which I projected a shopworn image of New York as a forbidding mystery, slowly disintegrated. I made it a goal to extend the boundaries of the comfort zone. Another cliché: learn the real New York.

I started taking the trains downtown every so often. Maybe two or three times a month I'd go down to Union Square and walk around the Strand or go down to Washington

Square Park. I'd venture off to SoHo or Little Italy, walking around listening to music in my headphones. I'd sit in Madison Square Park just to read. One time I was riding the 1 downtown on a particularly packed day, a Friday afternoon in early winter, a recipe for certain discomfort. But the experience was part of making me a New Yorker, not just a tourist. A young business-looking woman was sitting on the yellow and orange seats. I was standing, holding the overhead bar a few people over. She stood out because she was wearing a luxurious, almost-obnoxious fur coat and heavy red lipstick. You realize very quickly that New York's rich people don't actually ride the train. They're in cars on the surface. Those among the subway hordes who look rich and make you wonder what their apartments look like and what their job titles are — they're not rich. Even if they're better off than the rest of us (not always the case), they're still not doing well enough to escape the MTA. The train continued along its rigid route, and more people crammed in, all of us in a liminal phase between destinations. A young Black girl of maybe nine or ten with a large backpack got on the train, coming home from school, I assumed. She scooted in towards the middle, excusing herself though taking up little room. The fur-coated woman smiled at the young girl and stood up, offering her seat. Subway cars are plastered with posters promulgating a code of civility that calls for giving up seats to the elderly, disabled, and pregnant, but there's nothing in it about little kids. They're supposed to be spry and able-bodied, willing and ready to stand for hours. The woman's gesture thus struck me as that of a voluntary New Yorker acknowledging herself as inferior, in this context, to an involuntary New Yorker. Those born here have a higher place in certain hierarchies.

The girl sat down and immediately put her hands on the woman's coat. I watched, expecting a confrontation.

Wow, what is this? It's so *soooft*, she said.

The woman, standing, laughed and smiled. It's chinchilla actually.

Oh I love it. It's so nice.

Thank you very much.

What could have been a scolding took on the aspect of a teachable moment, the fur-coat lady reassuming primacy as quickly as she had relinquished it. *Listen up, little girl, if you work hard like me and put your best foot forward, you, too, can afford to wear the hairs of cute little animals.* A much-needed testimonial on behalf of late capitalism.

The girl rubbed her face in the coat. The woman laughed.

It just feels so nice!

There were no parents around to apologize for the child's behavior. The woman didn't seem to mind, though. They struck up a quick conversation, talking about school. It was almost nice to see. Then the girl asked, Do you want to see my impression of a homeless person?

The woman didn't answer, unsure how to proceed.

The girl hunched over and put her right hand out as if holding a cup. Excuse me, she coughed, attempting to make her young voice old and gravely. Can you please spare some change?

The woman smiled and stared straight ahead. I watched from afar.

I've got cancer and I've got no money. Please can you spare

some change? I need to go to the hospital or I'm going to. . . I'm going to *die!*

I got off the train at the next stop before the encounter had run its course. But I had seen enough to have gotten an object lesson in the hard-won maturity of New York's young natives.

As the oniony smell of the leftover everything bagels wafts through the sterile room, I am reminded that time is moving. That a speaker has been speaking. Only a few minutes have passed since I last checked. We break quickly for coffee. A 25-minute respite between morning sessions. Everyone shuffles to the back of the room, where large carafes sit on tables with white linens soon to be stained. Noise builds as everyone converses, still catching up even after two days together. I stay in my seat.

My head rears back with an enormous yawn. As I resettle my view, Vanek materializes in the aisle next to me with his hand on the table, leaning over casually and calmly. He smiles.

Hi Mr. Vanek. How are you doing today?

He nods.

Out of his pocket he takes a small folded piece of paper and sets it down in front of me. I unfold it and see pictures of the board members, the SBO elite, the Supreme Council.

In tiny red font, the page reads, The SBO Asks You For Your Support For The Following Candidates For Our Executive Committee For The Next 4 Years.

At the top there is a picture of Vanek. Henry Vanek, President. Then my father. Sergei Mercy, Vice President. I scan down the page and, as I feared, my face stares back at me. Graham Mercy, Secretary Treasurer. The picture is from a dinner with my family after my college graduation. I recognize it instantly because of the restaurant's floral wallpaper, which is decidedly not Wilkes-Barre. My mother really liked this picture and had a stack of 5x7's printed from Walgreens the day we got home. Everyone in our family got one. Whoever made this SBO roster sheet has cropped tightly around my face, removing any trace of my family. It's now just me standing there. My expression in the picture is out of character, a full-faced smile with teeth. That's how you know I was truly happy in that moment.

The floral backdrop marks me as an outlier on the Executive Committee, all the other members' headshots having monochromatic backdrops. Maybe Vanek wanted to make my image so dreadfully conspicuous that anyone who even glances at it will be impelled to scan the page in search of the superseded board member. Phil Hubik's disappearance is spelled out in the photo array's negative space, and my mug is there to underscore it.

I wonder what my dad would think, whether he would empathize with Hubik or with Vanek. I tend to believe he would not be happy: Vanek wouldn't threaten to fire him on my account if he could be trusted to go along with the scheme. Did Vanek know my dad would try to protect me from this?

Vanek pulls out his notepad and pen.

WE WILL PASS THESE OUT TOMORROW BEFORE

All right, thank you, Mr. Vanek.

We stare at each other.

Thank you, I repeat.

He nods.

Do you think there's a chance that this won't pass? Are you worried about that at all?

He shakes his head.

OK thank you again, Mr. Vanek.

Vanek puts away his notepad and tucks the pen into his shirt pocket. He turns his back and starts to leave.

Oh Mr. Vanek, one more thing — where did you get this picture of me from?

Mom, he mouths, pointing towards the door.

I take the paper, fold it four times, and put it in my pocket.

Dad: Our final speaker this morning is our actuary from TLN Actuaries, Robert Moore. He just got here form Connecticut this morning. And an actuary is really the heart of our organization.

Moore: Ah you're making me blush!

(*Laughter.*)

Dad: He tells us what we can sell our policies for, he tells us the rates, he critiques our organization. But he's the man. Rob Moore. Thank you.

Moore: Thank you. I was a little offended by the fact that you said the best part of the meeting is the breaks, knowing I was coming up to speak. So hopefully I'll turn your opinion around after this. I know this is the first time that I've been to your convention. It's usually Roger White. As you can tell, I am not Roger White. First, I am a lot taller. I'm probably not as loud. And although Roger will not agree with this, I am a lot younger (*Laughter*). I'm going to go over some of the important financial and membership results. I was told that Sergei read Henry's report before, which covered some of it, but I'm going to do it with pretty pictures, so hopefully it will be clearer and we can get some good ideas on the trends that we're talking about. I'm going to have some very good news to talk about, and I'm going to have some bad news to talk about. And I'm also going to talk a little bit about what an actuary does, and then I'm going to give you some important information about how you can live longer. So it won't be all business for us. Before we get to the good part of the talk, I'm going to talk about what's in my report. So everyone should have one — Lauren promised me that everyone would have a copy of my report, and so if you can pull that out we'll jump right into it. (*Papers shuffle.*) So the first thing I want to talk about is the financial situation. And, uh, the first graph on page 1: that's your surplus and it shows how the surplus has gradually changed over the last 10 years, and surplus is now up over $3 million. For those of you who don't understand what surplus is, surplus is the amount by which your assets exceed your liabilities. So if you think about your personal life, your own net worth, add up all the assets you have — all your stocks, your bonds, your 401k's, your cash — and then you subtract everything you owe — your mortgage, car loan, credit cards. So whatever you have left, that's your net worth. This is the SBO's net worth. And we want this to grow and we want this to be big. And so right now the SBO is certainly heading in the right direction, as you can see on that graph. The main catalyst for the recent increase in surplus was that you sold the old home-office building in Philadelphia, made a nice profit on it. You gained a lot because of the sale of that building, and you reinvested in bonds and stocks, which John Stinton is now in charge of. Uh, you have almost $3 million in surplus, that's 30 per cent more than you had in 2008. It would be even larger if not for some of the work I do as the actuary, where I have to set up initial liability of $600,000 extra reserves because some of the risks that we exceed in your liabilities. If not for that reserve, the 2008 surplus would have increased by even more. So the second graph on, uh, page 1 is the trend in assets over the last ten years. Here we can see a nice trend, a nice upward trend. This is all your bonds, your stocks, your cash, and the value of the new home office that you purchased. The assets have increased by about 50 per cent since 2008, and several factors contributed to that. You sold the home-office building and picked up a profit on that, you have gains on your common stock over the last 10 years, and you'd have an influx for annuities, which brings in cash to the organization. So you have over $14 million worth of assets — it's at an all-time high. We're doing a great job and I believe we can continue to keep that up. Things will look even better as the economy makes a full recovery. The next few graphs are not as good. And that is the membership graphs. And this is where I talk about the bad news.

The second graph on page 2 shows the trend in the number of policies enforced over the last 10 years. Uh, and we can see since around 2010 there's been a fairly steady decline in membership. You now have 33,679 life and annuity policies. Of course, it's a decrease of almost eight per cent since 2007. And so, as Sergei said earlier, it's very important that this number not continue to go down. We have to get that number to turn around and start increasing. I'd like to give these next two graphs just to give you an idea of how old the membership is. Uh, the first graph shows the attained age of the members by the life insurance, and the second graph is the attained age of the members for the annuities. And so if you look at that first graph there's 460 people — 467 policies, to be exact — where they're 80 and older. And then you look at the younger ages like, for example, at 40-49 there's only 280 policies enforced, so it shows that you're skewed to the older ages, that you really need to bring in some younger members. And this is a problem for a lot of small, uh, fraternals. On the annuity side, you wouldn't expect a lot of young people to be buying annuities, so we can see that the annuities are more towards the older ages. About 40 per cent of the membership is over age 60, only 30 per cent is under age 30. As membership declines, the matter of insurance enforced, as seen as the graph at the bottom of page 3, has leveled off at a little more than $17 million. $17 million. The current ground is still at an all-time high, but it hasn't been growing like you'd expect from a growing organization. Number of policies enforced has been decreasing because the society does not sell enough policies. I can't emphasize this enough. This is what the graph on top of page 4 shows, how few policies you sold since 2008. In 2012 you only sold 39 policies. That's about three policies a month. So you can't keep going on and surviving as an organization if you're not going to bring in new policies. The year before was only 54 policies. So you're not going to be able to grow surplus, grow your assets, if you don't start to sell more policies. This isn't a problem just for the SBO. This is a fraternal-wide problem. Whether you're a large fraternal or a small fraternal. But just because everyone else is having this problem is no reason for you to raise your hand and say, Meh, we're just like everybody else, we don't have to do anything about it. You really have to do something about it. The declining membership is getting the attention of the Pennsylvania State Insurance Department, and Lauren has sent me a letter that you received from the department, dated May 3. And it just had two questions on it. One of them, a very simple question, says, Can you please comment on any specific strategies that the society is currently employing to combat declining premiums and decreased membership? So this is getting the attention of the department, and you're going to have to do something to show them that you're trying to increase your membership, otherwise they're going to want to encourage you to, uh . . . merge.

Ollie is standing in the lobby waiting as I turn the corner. Everyone else shuffles behind me going to lunch, waiting on their hoagies and chips for the second day in a row, while

Ollie and I walk out the front door. It's 90 degrees outside, a disgusting summer heat, but we walk out unfazed, excited for our planned adventure.

What'd you think of everything this morning? I ask.

Dreadfully boring. Nothing new there.

Ha yeah. I don't really get the point of all this. They just beat us over the head with information and then feed us. Then we have a party, vote, and leave. Where's the democracy in that?

I don't think there is any, she says. I think it's just to make everyone feel good. Get everyone drunk, get everyone feeling involved, fight an inevitable death. There's no way that a Slavic fraternal life insurance company is going to survive when their solution is making an app so kids will join. As a kid, that insults me. No one is going to download an SBO app, especially not for fun.

We share a laugh.

Despite the darkness of our conversation, we're in high spirits. We're being purposefully bad, a feeling that we probably should have outgrown a few years ago. An innocent type of bad, worse than telling a lie but not as bad as physical violence. It feels good. We are going to commit breaking-and-entering and we don't care.

The car doors open and we enter into a warmth so condensed it has a weight to it. We move through it as if we're sliding into jelly, smooth and viscous. I turn on the car right away and the vents blast even hotter air. Ollie yelps with delight.

Sorry!

It's OK, it's OK!

We make a quick trip around the Square, barely talking, rolling down the windows and using the rushing air as a harsh fan. I continue down Market Street and take a right onto River past the Sterling. There are chain-linked fences around the front of the building guarding the decrepit hotel. We take a right into a parking lot, the random bank lot with the Masonic temple in the back, also defunct and decrepit.

All right, you ready to do this?

Yeah! Come on, let's go. Don't even give yourself time to second-guess it. You won't do it then.

OK, OK, I say while opening the door. We speak over the roof of my car. I just feel like . . . it's noon or whatever on a Saturday. In broad daylight. This can't be a good idea.

No that's better, they won't be expecting it. Come on, let's go.

The Sterling sits undisturbed, seven stories of greyish concrete weathered and dirtied by time, unclean and unaware of its impending doom. The sign out front, a black and white italicized *STERLING HOTEL* between two red and white crowns, extends over the sidewalk. The entire front of the building sits in a shadow cast by itself.

We walk toward the hotel, looking over our shoulders as if about to commit a heist. I'm trying to play it cool, unsure whether it's working. We're here. We're going to do it.

Between the hotel and the building next door is a small alleyway blocked by a chain-linked fence. I look around: no one is walking by, just cars driving one by one. The fence winds around to the alleyway, stopping at the edge of the neighboring building, which is set back slightly farther from the sidewalk than the hotel. Right beyond the fence is an open window into the Sterling, the makeshift plywood having been removed, presumably, by previous trespassers.

Quickly, without giving myself time to think, I grab the edge of the fence, its metal hot to the touch, and pull it towards us, creating a gap at the corner. The bottom scrapes against the concrete, making a harsh and sharp noise. I look around one more time, still no one walking around. Wilkes-Barre is a driving town despite, or perhaps because of, its marginal size. Cars continue to move past us, unwavering, towards their destinations. I look at Ollie and move back, a gentleman allowing his lady to go first. She scuttles through the tiny opening between fence and brick and into the alley. I follow behind her, making sure to leave the fence ajar.

The open window is about four feet off the ground with a small concrete ledge. I kneel down and without discussion offer my hands for Ollie's feet. She puts all her weight onto my hands and I hoist her so her right foot can rest on the ledge. She pushes herself upward while gently grabbing my shoulder, our first touch. I don't have time to enjoy it. She grabs hold of the window's concrete jamb as she finds her footing on the sill, hopping down into the abyss a second later. I jump, plant my hands, and with a downward press swing my left foot onto the ledge. My right foot follows and I'm perched on the window now. I stand upright, calibrating my balance. I see Ollie waiting below in a concrete room full of junk. She moves off to the side and I jump down in and join her. Upon landing on the filthy floor, I clap my hands, producing a small cloud of dust. Afterward, they're still stained grey.

Wow, so this is it.

What do you think?

I'm not sure yet, I whisper, as if someone could catch us now.

We walk through a doorway and find ourselves in the lobby. It's a large, bare room. The floor is plywood, damp and moldy. Bits of the ceiling, which is elegantly coffered, have fallen into heaping piles throughout the room. Roman columns support a balcony opposite the grand front entrance. Against the sunlight shining in through upper-floor windows above us and through cracks in the boarded-up windows at eye level, the columns, piles of debris, and up-ended fixtures cast a baroque tableau of shadow upon the concrete walls. The daylight, once inside the building, is warm and orange. There's graffiti everywhere, typical signs of teenage debauchery (a circled red anarchy A, a giant penis) and more thought-out pieces of wide bubble letters and shadows.

Wow, Ollie says under her breath. She takes out her phone and takes a picture. Stand over there, let me get your picture in here, she says.

Oh I don't know, I don't need a picture here.

Don't be such a baby! Come on, just stand right here. She points toward an area of light in the middle of the room.

OK, OK! I smile. She touches the screen of her phone and snaps the photo. Perfect, you look good. All right, let's keep going.

We move toward a wide set of stairs with railings of ornate filigreed ironwork. The base of the stairs is shrouded in shadow but as we approach the top we return to the light. We pause to look back down to the first floor. From this vantage, the building's miserable condition is in sharp relief. Forty-one years of neglect. We return to the stairs and continue our ascent.

We approach the light source, the west-facing windows on the building's façade, and as we pass an open door we see the Susquehanna River from three floors' height. The Market Street Bridge looks majestic. The greenery on the Kingston side of the river is lush. From up here, the city looks like a city, all grace, grandeur, and beauty. There are empty sleeping bags on the floor and jugs of partially drunk Turkey Hill Iced Tea thrown about. Neither of us mentions the mess.

I know we're in a dilapidated building, but everything looks pretty nice up here, I say.

Yeah it does. I like it.

There is not that much to see in an abandoned building, we soon realize. We move through the upper floors room by room, looking at the same things over and over again: dirt and dust and trash. The reality of the state of affairs starts to set in the more time we spend inside.

I can't help feeling like this is an allegory for something, this building, I say. The Hotel Sterling, a building that I never even really knew but was always there. A site of so much cultural importance for this area. This is what it looks like. Broken down and beaten up. It's kind of sad. It's like this is what happens to a place that no one takes care of, when the people in a town aren't even taken care of. There's no economy here, no workforce, nothing keeping anybody here other than cheap rent.

You should write something about it, a story or something. Like all about Wilkes-Barre.

I laugh. Yeah maybe I should.

Roland Barthes wrote an essay, called "The Reality Effect," about description in literature as a means of making the imaginary feel realistic. The premise of his argument is that discussion of insignificant objects and events in a story engenders in the reader a perception of the fiction as being in some sense "real": the accretion of seemingly arbitrary aesthetic decisions produces what we call believability. I read the essay in a creative-writing class. The discussion that followed was pretty straightforward — how to make your writing seem real, something that the young writers, especially me, were having difficulty with. After that class, we were assigned a short exercise: sit in a place, any place — a dorm, a coffee shop, the dining hall — and then just write about what it looked like and what was going on. Think about what things made it come to life. This exercise coincided with my aforementioned inward turn toward writing about the ordinary life I knew: Wilkes-Barre, teenage existentialism, whatever — plotless stories about places, ideas, and people, no spectacular climaxes or gotcha moments, just me trying to figure out what made my own life real beyond superfluous details and flowery prose. Once, after I'd submitted a story of this type to workshop, a fellow student refused to speak during my in-class critique. He just passed me his critical letter as the session was breaking up. These letters were our homework, presented to both student writer and professor as proof of our having actually read the stories under discussion. The typical format was to mention something you liked, something you didn't like, a way to improve it, and some reading recommendations. Preparing the letters was by far the most difficult part of the course: as reader, you had to come up with something new every time; as writer, you'd end up with 15 different people coming up with 15 different ways of conveying the inevitable mix of grudging, vague praise and extremely pointed criticism. The student who hadn't even bothered to speak in class wrote me the following feedback: I don't mean to spew nasties but your work is boring. Why would anyone care to read about something boring?

Barthes' essay argues that literary "reality" ultimately compromises a text's meaning: the details that try to create reality signify nothing. Without a signified, life is invoked in the absence of any living, breathing entity. The story may feel "real," but the reality is fake. Barthes was talking about more than just literary fiction, of course — his analysis was to be applied also to the narrative of life. The painting we paint, the picture we create. But in the story the silent guy called boring, I was talking *about* boredom. I wasn't casting around for random objects just so that I could describe them for literary effect; I was drawing from my real life, looking for where the signifier might coexist with the signified. Boredom, I had believed, must be more real, or at any rate more worthy of being called real, than a description of an arbitrary piece of furniture. Boredom is something that actually occurs in life. And it's especially prevalent in suburban America, where families have earned — or plundered — their peace and quiet. That's why Ollie and I are exploring the Sterling right now. Breaking into condemned buildings epitomizes suburban boredom. Clearly people have been doing this for a long time, coming into this place and looking around with either a very loose exploratory, maybe even destructive, agenda or none whatsoever. No one wants to invest the money into renovating, so us bored and curious people will explore it as a way to understand our past, or just as a way to kill a few hours. Or maybe to impress a girl.

I pick up a random piece of plaster lying on the floor and throw it at the wall. It explodes with a puff of dust and a loud bang. Ollie jumps.

I wasn't expecting that! she says. We laugh an honest laugh. She bends over and picks up another scrap of plaster, tossing it up and down, calculating its heft. Pretty heavy, she says.

Yeah, I mean, it was part of a 100-year-old building. It was holding this place together until right now.

The plaster is gray and chalky, shedding dust with each toss. Ollie starts to wind up like a Major League pitcher: she lifts her left foot in a stylized motion, as if she's stepping on an imaginary stool, and then hurls the thing forward, her entire body rolling over the fulcrum of her right foot on the follow-through.

Another thud, this one louder. More dust.

Wow you've got a real arm on you.

I played softball pretty seriously my whole childhood.

Look at you, I say.

We turn to face the incoming late-day sunlight and glance again at the river below. I bend over and look for something else to throw. I come up holding a two-thirds-intact brick.

Feel this one, I say, tossing it to Ollie.

She catches it with an oof. OK, this one is heavy, she says.

How does a brick even get inside a building? Aren't they supposed to be on the outside? I ask.

Beats me, I'm not an architect.

No just an expert on ancient apes.

Ha! It sounds so mean when you say it.

No! I really think it's cool. I think you're . . . cool, too. I keep thinking I'll outgrow awkwardness with age and I keep discovering it's still a part of me. It's been really nice getting to hang out with you the last two days, I say.

I've enjoyed it too, Graham. Thanks for showing me around your town.

We stand there. I'm tapping my fingers against my leg, she's twisting her foot into the floor. My cold sore starts to pulsate.

Think fast! she says as she turns, winds, and releases in one fluid motion, lobbing the brick at nothing in particular.

I follow with my eyes as the brick chunk skips and spins toward the window facing River Street. My eyes widen, waiting for the sound, which comes sooner than I calculated. The brick is through the window now and falling, I presume, directly into traffic, some four or five stories below.

Fuck!

Quick, we gotta get outta here. Come on, come on, come on!

I lead the way. We sprint down the old stairs, moving in and out of the darkness as we negotiate the landings, turning 180-degree hairpins and holding tight to the railing on each successive stage of the descent. We reach the bottom of the main stairwell, its grandness now just a blur. We're in the lobby again, disoriented by our exertion.

Which way did we come in?

Over here, this way.

We run into the room we entered through and leap, one after the other, onto the ledge unassisted. Ollie is first into the alley and books it for the fence, and I'm right behind her. We squeeze through the narrow space and cut a hard right toward the car.

Hey, hey, hey! Slow down, don't run. You don't want to be even more suspicious.

The amount of traffic sputtering by on River Street is the same now as when we arrived. The pitch of radio noise undulates wildly, up then down, as cars drive past us with open windows. We make the parking lot and I unlock my car with a fake nonchalance, different from the version I was affecting when we got here, my whole body shaking as I open the door. We get in. The humidity has returned in our short time away but we say nothing about it, its presence not germane to our predicament.

I turn the key over and send the vehicle toward the back-side exit onto North Franklin Street, taking a left at the Free Mason Temple and then two more lefts so that we're now heading back toward the Sterling, returning to the scene of the crime out of a sick curiosity. Did the cops show up? Did anybody see us? Did it kill an innocent person driving by?

The car slows down at the light for Market and River, and we stare up at the hotel. It's still covered in shade. On the fifth floor, a freshly broken window is hard to make out for the shadows. I scan the road for the brick and see no sign of it. It must have fallen onto the awning. There are no police and no Good Samaritans inspecting the scene. I take a breath and start laughing, turning and looking at Ollie. The sun shines through the car window. She stares at me with an expression of shock that quickly dissipates into a rogue calm, a look that says I can't believe we just did that and I can't believe we'll get away with it.

We laugh and we laugh.

Korbel: So what I've been doing is going to grandparents or going to the godfathers or godmothers, the older generation, to try to generate, you know, policies for the youth of the parish. But I think we can all agree that we have a problem here. And we need to generate membership somehow. To date, in this calendar year, we have sold . . . now let me get this straight . . . We've sold 52 policies. Is that right? We had 31 policies prior to the convention.

Bridgemen: We had 29 prior to the convention.

Korbel: OK, correction, we had 29 policies prior to the convention. That isn't a good statistic, folks. Our goal for 2013 was — is — 104 new members, or 104 new policies. So we're not even halfway there and we're over halfway through the year. And that's including members that we've added since starting up the membership drive yesterday. I don't have any magic formula up here. I don't have any concrete answers. But we do have to do some kind of brainstorming. And we have to come up with some strategies so that we will continue as a fraternal and as an organization and that we have to somehow make ourselves attractive to the youth! And bring in younger people. So with that being said, uh, I just want to open it up as a forum. I would like to hear any of the delegates now, here. What has been working for you? Would you like to share with the delegation what has been working for you in your particular situation? So what I'm asking is: is there anybody out there that would like to volunteer? What's working out there in your lodge? Or what are you doing to promote membership in your particular situation? Yes.

Helen: Hi, I'm Helen, delegate 45. I'm also part of another fraternal organization and we — what we do is we have, actually, an entertainment fund. You can ask the members to pay $4 a month and that fund goes towards activities. So every year we do an event in New Jersey, rent out the Wonderland there, and bring a ton of kids and grandkids and cousins. We have the whole pier to ourselves for two hours. And they just do other smaller events throughout the year. Even if you did, like, say, an amusement park for the day, and if you signed up your grandchild or child then maybe they get half admission or something like that to incentivize them to sign up for a policy. And then we also advertise that all through a Facebook page so that people are in the know of what events are coming up. We try to do something quarterly.

Korbel: That's different. Thank you for sharing. Anybody else want to share what might be working in your particular situation? This is a topic that the board has been struggling with for quite some time now. So, we have, uh, discussed and discussed and tried to come up with strategies. The website is a work in progress, I would say, it's an ongoing process, but we're going to try and get that more, I think, updated and interactive. Try to get that more 21st-century savvy. So that could maybe be one way, but we still have to figure out where are we going to get more members from. As a delegate here at the convention, you have to realize that not only do lodge secretaries have the right or responsibility to sell policies — anybody here can go out and promote the SBO, anybody can sell a policy. We have a wonderful staff at the home office: Lauren, Melody, and Carol — they're great resource people. I call on them often as a board member, as an auditor, and, uh, they're top-notch folks. So we want you to get out of here and leave this convention maybe with a different mindset of, I have a responsibility as a member of the SBO to promote this fraternal into and well beyond the 21st century. We are all here because we want this, this fraternal to succeed. So we all have a responsibility, each one of us that is sitting here has a responsibility to go out there and go back to your home and to your lodges and if you need to brainstorm, sit down and say, What are we going to do to bring in new members into this organization? Father Dubinsky.

Father Dubinsky: All right. I want to preface what I'm going suggest with just a few things. I am one of those people who grew up loving everything there is to love about the Slavic heritage. I would hum along to the Red Army Chorus in my car listening to "The Anthem." I love Ivan Rebroff and I can fall asleep to him. I destroyed my thighs in the Russian Dance Group in Akron, Ohio, for a number of years. I was devastated in college when I found out that I was not 100 per cent per cent Russian but that I was in fact, like most of us here today, a Russian hillbilly of Carpatho-Russia. So I want to preface all that. And I also am grateful — very grateful — to this organization because they provided for my wife and I when we were sitting and hovering above the poverty line for St. Tikhon's Seminary, offering us two years' worth of financial assistance through scholarships. I'm very, very grateful for that, for all of the fellowship and whatnot. My suggestion, and I made this a couple years ago, is in line with a comment made by our actuary earlier, something I found to be very eye-opening. He said that something has to change. And I brought up a couple years ago — kind of more in private to the board and with his Beatitude, Metropolitan Thurston — about the name Slavic Brotherhood Organization. You can see it in all of the recent paperwork and all of the bags that we have here today. It no longer says Slavic Brotherhood Organization, it says SBO. However, I've run into the issue when I discuss this organization with people — and I'm in the Midwest — my parish is made up of probably 60-70 per cent American converts and 30 per cent — I've got Greeks, Serbs, Bulgarians, Albanians, and maybe one Russian — and when I say, "Would you like to join or talk about some of the benefits of the SBO," they say, "What is the SBO?" And I say, "It is the Slavic Brotherhood Organization." And regardless of what I say after — I can say it's a three per cent gain, your kids can get scholarships, you can have all these wonderful things — as soon as you hear the name Slavic, all of that is turned off. I am . . . I love the Slavic culture,

I love the Slavic heritage, and I love everything there is to love about Eastern Orthodoxy and the traditions, the music, the Slavonic. I'm born into it, I love it. But I use the sign example. There's a street in Akron and on this street there are four Orthodox churches within a mile and a half of each other. One mailbox actually neighbors the next mailbox, and you drive down this street and you see Presentation of Our Lord, Romanian Orthodox Church, and then you drive down the street and you see St. Demetrius, Serbian Orthodox Church, and then you drive just a little bit farther and it says St. George Antiochian Orthodox Church. And if I am a person who is of none of the descents and I am looking to join an organization or, more specifically in that instance, a church, I am going to find the one that has no ethnic identity. That's the one I'm going to join. And so I just would bring it to the board and I know you've done a lot of work on this, but the excuse in the past has been that it would cost too much money to change the name in some of the contracts and all of the different bylaws. But we just got a surplus of money from the sale of this house and I offer this as a humble suggestion for the board to consider changing the name to Christian Brotherhood Organization so you could better market to those who are not Slavic. Nobody's coming in off the boat anymore, folks. And in our churches, we still need to minister to those already here. But if we're going to be able to promote this, especially to our churches and especially past the East Coast, going more into the Midwest and the West, there are no more Russians in these churches. No more Slavs. So I just leave that for consideration.

Korbel: Thank you, Father Dubinsky, for your comments. That will be noted. We actually did discuss it at one time — the name change — but that is still . . . We need to work on that.

Everyone from the convention assembles in the conference room for the group photo. The photographer is up on a yellow ladder, already scanning the room for the best angle, his flashes set up just right. People mull around just as they do during the breaks, though now everyone is dressed in their Sunday best for Saturday night. Suits and dresses, ties and broaches. One man, an enormous, bald man from somewhere in Ohio, wears a tuxedo for some reason. He's been wearing a T-shirt and jeans the whole weekend so far.

The crowd has naturally gathered in front of the photographer. My parents are with the Organization board and I stand there as I have for the rest of the convention: slightly confused.

All right, everybody, we're going to need to get you all together to take this photo. I know I'm the one standing between you and dinner, so let's help you help me get this done quick. Tall people to the back, shorter people to the front. Make sure you can see your leaders there in the middle.

The crowd starts to shape-shift.

OK, I'm going to need you over here. The photographer starts pointing at individuals and families, moving them around as the mass of people continues to writhe and swell and contract. All right, OK, this is looking good. He looks into his camera and snaps a test photo, causing the flashes to go off. Everyone is blinded.

You! Over there, the young man.

I point at myself. Me?

Yes, you! Come over to the middle here. You'll be the star of the show.

I shuffle out of my little corner and go to the middle of the group, in front of the platform that the executive board is standing on. A hand places itself on my shoulder. I look up. Vanek. Smiling down on me.

Oh hello, Graham, Mrs. Vanek says.

Hey kid, my dad says.

Staying out of trouble? Mrs. Vanek asks.

I turn around. Trying to, I say.

Hey, guy! Camera's over here!

I turn around and offer a smile to the photographer. Vanek pats my shoulder again.

The flashes go off.

Perfect! says the photographer.

Dad: It is an honor to stand here and welcome you to the Slavic Brotherhood Organization's Grand Banquet in celebration of our 100th year. While we are all enjoying this wonderful meal in this very nice hotel, it might be hard to imagine how much things have changed. But things are much different from those earlier years. Shared rooms and bathrooms at Roba Farms, no air conditioning, no delegate expenses, and bring-your-own-liquor are some of the fables from the past. You can see how different that is today. The SBO has been around since 1913, and we were born out of necessity in Mahanoy City, Pennsylvania, to provide benefits for deceased miners. I'm told that when a coalminer died, his body was dropped on the front porch of the company house, leaving a distraught and penniless widow to bury her husband. Welp, we've come a long way in 100 years. From the pennies and nickels scrimped and saved by our ancestors and the fine management of the present and past officers of the SBO, the SBO has become the stable and profitable organization it is today and the envy of other fraternal life insurance companies. Please enjoy your dinner and music by the Southeast Pennsylvania Balalaika Orchestra.

The banquet, or the Gala Banquet as it's called in the program, is in the same room as the rest of the convention, and a loose feeling of déjà vu takes over as we re-enter the familiar space now made different. Round tables with slip-covered chairs stand where the long, rectangular tables and rolly chairs were, just an hour or so before. What was once a place of calm and putative concentration is now passed off as a place of elegance and revelry. The floral centerpieces are tasteful yet unnervingly large. The wait staff are dressed in formal wear.

The small balalaika orchestra, five players, is set up in the corner of the room and begins performing as we take our seats. The costumed group plays a slow song on the triangular three-stringed instruments, all five members picking with a ferociousness that, in juxtaposition to their expressionless faces, produces an air of deadpan mockery. I imagine they are all high school band and math teachers. They're bearded and glassesed and there's no way this pays their bills. This first song, an unabashedly Russian number, sounds so impossibly sad. The chords are minor and the melody feels fatalistic, as if there's no escaping the key, no matter how hard the musicians try — as if depression has been built into their instruments. Everyone sits and enjoys the music, relishing its sadness and admiring its beauty. All very Russian. I'm still looking for a seat. I spot Ollie but her table has no vacancies. The chair to her left is occupied by her father, who is staring impassively into the middle distance while Mrs. Hubik, seated to his left, whispers in his ear. To Ollie's right sits a barrel-chested middle-aged man with a thinning grown-out buzzcut and a Tom Selleck mustache, his napkin tucked into his collar like a bib, his hands cupped around his mouth as he repeatedly shouts, in the direction of the far-away head table, a Russian surname I can't quite make out, his ample cheeks flush with the color of a ripe pomegranate. I walk toward to the table, resigning myself to a quick hello.

Hello Graham, Phil Hubik says as I approach. Enjoying the weekend?

Hi, how are you? Yeah I'm having a good time, I say back, shaking his hand.

Hi Graham, Ollie says.

Hey. I move over behind her seat.

Sorry it looks like the table's full. I tried to save you a seat but my parents' friends all piled in.

Don't worry about it. You want to head out again after dinner? Go for a walk or something?

Ollie smiles. Yeah I'd like that.

OK I'll just come grab you when this is winding down.

Sounds good, see you later then.

I move away from the table, still without a place to sit. There's an almost entirely empty table not far away. The actuary, who spoke earlier in the day, sits unescorted across from an older couple who are not acknowledging him. His speech was pretty good, too.

Is this seat taken? I ask.

No, please take a seat.

Hi, I'm Graham Mercy, I say. Sergei's son.

Oh nice to meet you. I'm a big fan of your dad, he does great work. A pleasure to work with. I'm Rob Moore.

Thank you. I sit down. You know I enjoyed your speech earlier today.

Oh that's kind of you, glad you liked it.

We exchange awkward but kind smiles and nods, unsure how to start a conversation that might span the wide generation gap between us.

So you in school?

No. I actually just finished up this past May. Out in the real world now, just looking for a job is all.

Oh wow, congrats. Where'd you go?

I went to Columbia.

Wow that's a good school. Ivy League. Your mom and dad must be really proud of you.

Yeah I hope they are.

I'm coming from Connecticut myself. My wife and I used to go to the city a lot when we were younger because it's not too far. Just take the train in, you know. Then we had kids and it became too much of a hassle, trying to wrangle toddlers in Midtown or something was a bad scene. We go in for a play and dinner sometimes still, but not as much as we used to. Now Audrey, my oldest — she's 17 — is getting ready to apply for college and she's dead set on going to New York. She doesn't really care what school it is as long as it's in the city. I think you got to be young to be able to do that.

Yeah I guess it's a pretty hectic place to be.

You guess? He affects a laugh.

I mean I was on the Upper West Side, in Morningside Heights. That's not like really being in the middle of any action.

That's fair, that's fair. I guess when people think of the real craziness of New York they're thinking of Times Square.

Yeah. Don't get me wrong, New York has a lot going on. There's people everywhere all the time. But I could still go sit on a bench in Morningside Park for an hour and only see a handful of joggers go past me. The areas I spent most of my time in were pretty residential and pretty subdued, it felt like. Still, though, it's completely different from Wilkes-Barre.

I can see that. But so you were up there for Hurricane Sandy? How was that?

Yeah that was last year. We honestly weren't even touched. It's wild because I know downtown they really got it bad.

Like some of the trains are still messed up because of it. But we just had a bunch of rain, maybe some tree branches were taken down. They canceled class for two days. Obviously that was the right move, I'm sure some professors were stuck in their apartments with no power or something off campus, but it really didn't seem like anything was going on at the time. I couldn't understand the seriousness of the situation, even though just a few miles away it was just destroying things. There's a big joke at school that there's a "Columbia bubble," this imaginary constraint that keeps students stuck on campus. But it seems like the bubble actually helped keep us safe this time around.

We had a national emergency called in Connecticut too, but we were in the same boat, didn't really get hit that hard at all. We probably had it just as bad as you, some downed branches and heavy rain, but nothing to worry about it when it was all said and done. We were keeping up with it on the news, seeing how powerful and devastating the storm was. We were in the same storm, though, but we didn't get hit that bad. It's kind of surreal, you know? It's strange how like the true, real Sandy was so different than the one that we both saw but we still all saw the same hurricane. I feel like the storm we saw should've had a different name or something.

Ha, yeah, we got Hurricane Stuart instead, Hurricane Sandy's nicer younger brother. I always find it strange that we give them human names, though. It makes the damage feel worse than like a random act of nature. More personal.

Yeah I know some guys who talk about their first wives that way. "Sandy ruined everything."

I smile at the joke.

The balalaika orchestra starts playing the song from Tetris.

My dad gets up on the stage and taps the microphone three times. The Executive Board is seated at the head table, which is on a riser at the front of the room, more or less the same setup as for the meetings earlier. They're facing us but half the room has their backs turned to them. I turn my chair to face the podium.

Servers bring out salads. The romaine is pale and see-through under a bright orange dressing, some kind of roasted red pepper. I force my fork into the collage of vegetables.

Bon appetit, I say with my fork next to my face.

How do you say it in Russian?

I have no idea.

Dad: We didn't have dessert yet but we can continue with our program if you don't mind. And next we have . . . We asked Father Dubinsky to speak to us tonight and give us some remarks. He's been a fierce supporter of the SBO, faithfully attends conventions and attends events in the Western Pennsylvania and Ohio area when he can. He is the director of St. Andrew's Church in Akron, Ohio. Father Dubinsky.

Father Dubinsky: One of my elders was named Victor Hudak. He was a mayor of Lorimer, Ohio, in the 1940s. I used to visit Victor many, many times as a church chaplain. He taught me these three principles that I'm going to begin my little talk with, short and sweet. Henry Vanek asked that I share them with you. Number one — and I live my life by these three principles, Victor was one of the best men I met in my life — number one is fear no evil. Fear no evil. Number two, let no one steal your joy. And the third and last is the hardest: expect nothing and never be disappointed. Personally, my wife survived breast cancer at 46 years of age, I underwent coronary artery bypass surgery a few years ago, and every day that we are married we are called by God to rejoice in the Lord. I am happy to be here with you today to share these lessons. Now I'd like to begin my remarks.

Distinguished Executive Board, Supreme Council, and fellow clergy, SBO members, guests and friends — I've come to you this evening to extend my parish's and my personal thanks and congratulations on another successful, 25th annual convention of the Slavic Brotherhood Organization of the United States of America. I have been a member of the SBO for the past 20 years or so, having come into contact with Lodge 204, Akron, Ohio, through my friendship with Phillip Hubik, our national secretary and treasurer. The membership of Lodge 204 is very active and I'm able to participate in the many activities it holds each year, including quarterly and yearly meetings, golf outings — which I did just this last Saturday — Christmas celebrations, barbecues, and other events. It's the activities of the local lodge that get together all the time that have drawn me closer and closer. Phillip encouraged my wife and I to get involved in the SBO and purchase policies for my three children. Over the years, all three have been recipients of SBO scholarships as they went on to college and even post-graduate education. One short detail, the Archpriest Thomas Dubinsky, one of six priests in our family over 280 years of Eastern Orthodox priesthood, purchased a policy after his ordination some time in the 1950s. And we — his nine children, including my father and his brothers, nor myself — had no idea that he held such a policy until his death in 2007. I feel proud to be connected to my family through this proud organization, and to be connected to all of you through it as well. Having been able to attend the last several national conventions, I have been able to renew special friendships with many people who are once again here, including the Supreme Council members, such as Henry and Sergei and their wives, who I just saw at the 19th All American Council of the American Eastern Orthodox Church, where our SBO was a witness and a presence there. I'm sure that we will all agree that this organization is a well-tuned heart, that we try to ensure that there will always be a solid commitment to the future of effectively acquiring new members and new polices to grow our SBO and its assets. If you haven't had a chance — and I did, preparing these few words — to review the new website design, you will be impressed and made proud to see how well we are presented to the world. I also have come to understand through conversation with Phillip that there is an ongoing development for a member or a potential member to study and review the SBO's history, through videos and pictures, policies and membership information, and present them through our online website. I really feel, to repeat what Sergei has said, that this website will grow this fraternal well into the future, and let's pray for that. So I'm glad to say this evening, let's renew our commitment to not only attend these national conventions, which allow us to catch up with a solid management of policies and premiums, but to do all that we can to grow and reach out to others so that they may too enjoy the benefits of the SBO and the absolute family atmosphere that we know so well. My own parish of Saint Andrew's Eastern Orthodox Church of Akron, Ohio, has participated several years in the church deposit program, and I'm happy to announce that, after having sold the rectory that my family was living in, my parish will be investing at least another $160,000 into that SBO account.

May God grant the family-oriented membership of the SBO, its Supreme Council, the Executive Board, the actuaries with many happy blessed years. *Mnog hia letta*. I hope to see everyone here once every four years. Pray for our leadership and may everyone have a safe journey home after tomorrow morning's meeting.

Dad: Thank you, Father Dubinsky, for those inspiring words.

After dessert — a slice of cold vanilla cake — the balalaika players set their instruments down and go off to their own table to finally enjoy their food. My father approaches the lectern one last time while two other board members move the icon of Saint Alexis of Wilkes-Barre off the riser.

Dad: Thank you all again for your support of this Organization. We have prepared a short slideshow with the help of Lauren, showing the history and the growth of the SBO from old times to new. Again, thank you to Lauren for her help with this, as she spent a long time looking through photos and scanning them. A copy of this video will be posted on our website too, at the end of the convention, so please feel free to share it with your friends, family, or church. Think of it like a commercial. OK, someone please hit the lights!

A hotel employee standing near the stage turns the dimmer clockwise and the room goes dark. A screen drops from the ceiling and a projector comes to life. After a few seconds of nothing, the video begins. Another Russian song plays through speakers, this time with singing. Again, it's sad, but this time I think it's really meant to be. The SBO logo fades in on the screen.

Celebrating 100 years of the Slavic Brotherhood Organization.

The photos are black and white with visible rips and tears. Rows of men in suits fade into another, similar shot. Time passes as the slideshow continues. I don't recognize a single face. I suspect no one else does either. Now there is a group of men, three of them, in front of a church, wearing nearly identical nondescript suits, buttoned and incredibly stiff-looking. They stare straight into the camera. Cross-fade. A similar-looking group of men appears, stern and serious, standing in a nature setting, a backdrop of trees and sky. Now some sort of picnic: women in dresses have joined the severe men, and an old SBO banner is planted in the ground. Next, a picture of laughing women making food in a large kitchen, probably a church basement. The song changes.

The pictures evolve as the show goes on. They go from a faded black and white to, eventually, a warm and dated color photo in which men wear thick-rimmed glasses and women have large hairdos. Everyone in the frame is dressed well, unlike all extant photographs of me. Everything I've ever seen of my past self serves to remind me that I will one day look back and regret how I appeared on this day and time. We always feel so comfortable in the present, but once it's our past it becomes a lesson: I shouldn't have worn those shorts. I should have never gotten that haircut. These photos look timeless, though. They look period-appropriate. They look like they could never exist now.

I look around the room at all the people watching the screen. Maybe now they're getting to a period where they might recognize someone, an uncle or a mother perhaps. They look on in wonder and appreciation. It's impossible for me to think about the past without visualizing it in the style of contemporaneous photos and videos. When I see a picture from the turn of the 20th century, I can't help but imagine the world back then was actually in black and white and that all the motion was as herky-jerky as the Keystone Kops. Everything from the '60s has deep and rich colors; it's soundless and authentic-looking. And even the '90s, the decade of my childhood, which doesn't feel that long ago, has its own technologically determined look: memories being adjusted to tape tracking, a pre-digital stiffness that's already lost. My childhood memories come to me as if being played on an old VHS or developed from 35-millimeter film, the signified recollections subsumed by the available recording medium.

Our era, our current present, looks no different than what any photo's present looked like. I can't be the only one who sometimes almost forgets that. The bowler-hat crowds we see in the earliest film footage saw things back then as they really were, not as the primitive cameras of the day captured them. It's a useful reminder that, one day, all the hi-def imagery of our present-day selves, which seems so perfect and true to life, will be comically dated, a sign of how stupid we were to think we had captured the truth. I'm sure that Charlie Chaplin's first-run audiences thought his films looked just like real life. It took technological improvements to show them they were wrong. We just have to be conscious of what we're looking at, that it's the content of the photo that matters, not the way it looks. The past has always been hi-def. These pictures I'm looking at tonight aren't a cloak: they don't hide our past from us; they help expose us to it.

At the end of the banquet I see Ollie quickly. Everyone is leaving the grand ballroom to head to the party room, the runoff space that staff have been setting up as the bar. Still dressed in their formal wear, the men undo their ties slightly, or undo their top button, signaling that they're ready for the fun, some innocent adult debauchery.

Hey do you want to hang out now?

Hey! I just want to get changed quick, is that OK? she asks.

Yeah that's a good idea, I'll do the same.

OK great. Meet in the lobby in 15?

I'll be there.

My father is lingering around the front of the room by the icon of St. Alexis. I can see he wants to pull me into a conversation but I pre-empt him by asking for the room key. He pulls the card out of his pocket and hands it over and I run to the elevator.

Their room is on the third floor. The elevator moves slowly, pulling itself upward with an elegant lurch. I am alone. I burst through the doors at the first sign of their opening and run toward my parents' room, which is midway down the hall.

The room is nicely made. A short vacation but not one absent of kempt appearances. Even in the private confines of a hotel room a mile from her home, my mother organizes and tidies. The carpet is red and a chair of almost the exact same shade sits in the corner with my father's casual pants laid over them. My clothes, a pair of jeans and a T-shirt, lie sprawled over the floor.

I kick off one shoe and then the next while undoing my tie and trying to unbutton my shirt. I strip down to my underwear and look at myself in the reflection of the darkened television. The lights are harsh inside the room, but in the television I can barely make out any details. I can't see any colors, just a black reflection of the outline of myself nearly nude. I take off my undershirt and stand there bare-chested.

I am not having sex tonight. I don't want to. For some reason, though, it still crosses my mind. Another delusional fantasy. I have a cold sore busting out of my lip that is somehow still getting worse. I can't even have a kiss. That's not in the cards, I remind myself, nor was it ever. There is no reason to be nervous; nothing can happen. We are going to talk and we are going to do the same thing we've been doing — nothing wrong with that. It's nice to talk, it's nice to have someone to talk to. When you don't have that kind of thing in your life, you can start to feel as if it doesn't exist. When I feel lonely, any time I feel sad or friendless, I forget that I have had and still have friends. For that matter, I have friends less than a mile from here, but since we're apart it's almost as if our friendship has ceased to exist and the history of its existence has been stricken from the record. The weight of any current moment outweighs any semblance of sentiment. My loneliness cannot be cured by past instances of comradery because they're not here right now, in the pre-eminent present, which is when I need them.

We meet in the lobby, both having returned to our normal selves notwithstanding some traces of formality clinging to Ollie — eye shadow still applied and hair still slightly curled. She is sitting in a large chair near the front door when I come down.

Hey you ready to get going?

Yeah of course.

We go out the front, the automatic doors separating as we approach, allowing us to enter the warm night. We have made the same trip now a few times but it's not yet familiar; it still feels exciting and new. The doors open to a world of possibility.

So what do you want to see tonight?

Oh I don't know, I just figured we'd walk around. Is there anything I should see? Anything that you think is really important here?

Not off the top of my head. I'm not sure if there's a whole weekend's worth of activities here. Maybe an afternoon's. But stretching all this out into a few days is hard, I only do the same few things over and over again. Besides, I don't really think we can top our visit to the Sterling.

Yeah . . . I'm sorry about throwing that brick through the window.

Nothing to be sorry for. We didn't get in any trouble so now it's just a memorable moment. Here, let's take a left.

We avoid the Square by turning onto Washington. The streets are completely desolate, no people are out, same tableau as before, though a little more desperate-looking in the dark. Still a few cars moving slowly about town — that's it, though. We continue down Washington under the warm-seeming glow of streetlights, passing the CYC on our left and the parking garage complex to our right.

OK so this whole building that we're coming up on, on the corner up there, that's this complex that they built for the movie theater. It took them forever to build the movie theater, I don't really remember why. It started when I was a kid. But basically this lot here was just dirt with a few iron beams in it for years. I guess that's a recurring theme here. And then finally, I don't know how, they got this whole complex built. They put up the movie theater that's just around the corner and then they built all these storefronts around it too. And then they put some apartments on top. I heard they wanted like $2,000 a month for a place in there. For an apartment. In Wilkes-Barre. You can get a whole house here for that. I don't really know what they're thinking. But this is their idea of the revitalization of downtown: throw in a movie theater and then magically everything will be working right again.

$2,000?

OK I'm exaggerating slightly for dramatic effect, yes, but still, it was more money than I'd be willing to pay.

Ha OK. Well it looks nice, at least there's that.

Yeah you're right, it looks nice. And I'm not even mad. I go to the movies here, I use the facilities and all. But it just seems to really miss the point. The town doesn't need a movie theater to keep it going. I don't know. And look, half of these storefronts are empty still. They can't even get businesses to move in.

What do you think it needs, then?

I'm not the mayor or anything, I don't know. I don't think the mayor knows either, though.

We continue onto Northampton, walking toward South Main Street. A few people linger outside the movie theater under the awning as we walk by.

I like it here, Ollie says. It's nice. It just feels like a small town.

Thanks, I'm glad you like it. Is it similar to where you're from at all?

Yeah I guess. I mean we didn't have the kind of natural disaster you had, but it's a town that's seen better days. I think it's just a Rust Belt thing. Everywhere I've been in Ohio and Pennsylvania has felt this way.

Yeah that's true. Do you want to stay in Pennsylvania after you graduate, or are you trying to move back to Ohio?

We slow down as we approach the intersection.

I'm not sure. I'm really thinking I'm going to keep going to school so it depends on where I get in, but none of the schools here are the top schools for what I want to study. UC Berkeley has a good program, Harvard obviously has a good program . . . Cornell . . . and Duke.

Those are all good schools.

Yeah that's the problem. I'm a little worried about even getting into them. So obviously I'll apply to some schools in PA, but I think if I'm able to go to any of those schools, the best option would be for me to leave.

I'm sure you'll get into whatever school you want.

We walk in silence for a few paces, unsure of what to say. I have no advice, no words of encouragement, I don't even know what I'm talking about, so I continue my tour.

So up here on the left is Wilkes University's campus. That's one of the two colleges we have in Wilkes-Barre. There's Wilkes, which is where my dad went, and then there's Kings, which is a Jesuit school. My dad didn't even want to go there, though. My dad wanted to go to Bucknell, actually, out in Lewisburg, but he thought he had to stay home to help run the house. I think he said the big thing was that he had to help his mom put coal in this ancient furnace they had every day. I guess she didn't know how to do it. My dad was taking care of the home, he was the man of the house. His dad died when he was only 15.

Oh I'm sorry to hear that.

Thanks, it's OK. It's way before I was born. But then my

dad graduated and he moved away to start a teaching job and my grandmother just got a gas furnace instead. Like he could've gone to Bucknell after all, I guess.

Yeah that's how it is sometimes. It seems like there's no other option but there usually is.

I nod in agreement.

We get to River Street again and cross toward the Susquehanna.

Oh you know what? I do have something to show you. Let's go left here, it's just at the end of the block.

We start walking down the street toward farther-off intersections, toward nothing in particular. We stop at a small post, a small blue sign. These historical markers are found throughout PA, always blue with yellow text and with the small equestrian logo on top. The sign reads: "Franz Kline (1910-1962) The Abstract Expressionist painter, born in Wilkes-Barre, helped establish the international reputation of American artists in the 1950s. Kline's 'Action Painting' is noted for bold, emotionally charged brushstrokes and non-representational subjects. The stark anthracite landscape of his native region inspired Kline's most famous work: his black and white paintings of the 1950s, including *Lehigh*, *Luzerne*, and *Pittston*."

This is that painter you told me about, right? Ollie asks.

Yeah. Franz Kline. That's him.

I stop and read it along with her.

So the area around here really influenced him? The coal and everything?

I mean, I'm not an expert, I don't know for sure. I don't really think he even spent too much time here. But if I had to guess, I feel like the years he spent here, when he was really young, were really important times, right? That's kind of how it always is, I feel.

Yeah I guess so.

I just think it's pretty cool. I must've passed by this sign so many times without stopping to read it. That's the cool part about this to me. It's been here forever, his art has been world-famous for decades before I was born, but I was never aware of it until a few years ago. And now there's all this stuff to discover. I like that idea that we could've walked the same places or seen the same things. There's a chance that if for some reason he came back to visit Wilkes-Barre very late in his life he even could have had Angelo's. I think they opened the year he died.

She laughs. Yeah that's pretty cool, I guess, sharing a pizza with your favorite artist.

There's this one painting he did — here let me show it to you. It's called *Horizontal Rust*. It's my favorite one. I reach into my right pocket to grab my phone. Let me look it up, I say, typing on the screen. Here it is.

We both stare at the painting: three harsh, thick black lines run horizontally across the bottom portion of the vertical white-painted canvas, forming an E under falling, diagonal lines coming from the top of the canvas. There is a muted brown — the titular rust, I suppose — that falls behind the top, horizontal black line. The movement of the painting is slow like molasses. The lines are enormous. The image radiates off my small rectangular screen, which I hold in portrait orientation, for optimal viewing of the canvas.

I think it's weird that the painting emphasizes the direction in its name. *Horizontal Rust*. But the painting is vertical. What is it about the direction that's important? Everything in this just seems so arbitrary, Ollie says.

It's kind of hard to tell what any of it means or is supposed to tell you. But the thing is with these paintings is that the title is really your only roadmap for interpretation. You can't just look at these lines and know what's going on. That doesn't really make any sense. Kline even rejected that idea. He wanted people to look at the work and be free from any sort of suggested meaning. He wanted people to feel the effect of the painting or something like that, to not have us bogged down by meaning.

Well what effects do you feel then?

I don't know exactly how I feel. It's hard to put it into words but I can try.

OK . . . go ahead.

I pause for a moment, crossing my arms and then wrapping part of my right hand around my chin, a thinking pose. All right, well . . . Do you remember what I said about that quote of his? That he paints the white as well as the black? So I look at this, and I think about the title and that quote, and I think that obviously that streak of color is really important to the work, even though it's subdued. And it's horizontal, the title tells us, so there is no real movement to it — it just keeps moving straight ahead, no real arc or motion. But the thing that gets me is that the rust is kind of hidden there. It's covered up by these two diagonal lines and it kind of feels like the black is painted over the top of it as well. Rust is about wear and tear, about aging, it comes from something sitting out in the elements, unprotected for a while and not being cared for. But in this it just fades into the black, it becomes part of something else. I can't help but think of Wilkes-Barre in looking at the painting. It's almost like your past is a part of you but it doesn't have to determine your future, or that it becomes part of your present, or something like that. That even bad or ugly or rusted things are part of you, that they still help in the creation of yourself. I don't know, I feel like I'm rambling now.

I think that makes sense. I get what you're saying. I'm thinking about it a little different, though.

OK good. You tell me what you think about it. I'd love to hear it.

OK, OK. I get what you're saying about the rust, about how it can be a sort of complicated past. That it is maybe even a part of their definition, but I'm just thinking that he didn't, like, disappear into the rust. That's what you said, right? It's not just supposed to be representative of his own experience, of his exclusive being — because if we couldn't relate to it then no one would care about it, what, 50, 60 years later? It's like, in my experience, I'm not studying ancient apes because I think they themselves are interesting. I do it because I think they have something to tell us about ourselves today. We're all part of the same thing, a continuum or constant existence. So I'm looking at this and I don't see a personal foundation but a foundation of people, of everything. Apes, mammals, plants, the planet as a whole, whatever. I don't see it as a moment disappearing into a person, it's more like . . . an entity disappearing into a larger whole. I feel like it's about connections. Even though we're different, we're all part of this same thing. Like this horizontal movement forward that you were talking about brings us all together.

Geez you look at the thing for 30 seconds and come up with something way more insightful than I have. And I've stared at it for like hours.

We laugh. Come on, don't put yourself down. I wouldn't have thought of that anyways without your starting it. Mine wasn't really based off the painting, I didn't see it in that. My response was more based off your reaction.

I return my phone to my right pocket. As I pull my hand back out, a piece of paper folded in fourths falls to the concrete, the paper from Vanek. Ollie reaches down and grabs it, my printed face staring back at her.

What's this?

My plan is exposed, this is where everything falls apart. She'll know that I'm taking her father's seat, that I'm actively engaged in a plot to inflict pain on her family. That I am in fact a man with a cruel heart, a malevolent spirit driven by insecurity and selfishness. I've put myself before her, before her father. I have betrayed her and I have done so willingly and unprovoked. I am worse than no good. I am bad. I have tried to take control of my narrative and I molested it. And now I am found out, seen for who I truly am. A headlight shines brightly and washes out the shadows on my face, revealing a man of ugly demeanor. I have no excuses.

It's, uh, a paper Mr. Vanek gave me. It's supposed to be the new board.

Oh . . . You're going to be on it?

Yeah. Vanek asked if I'd be involved.

That's great! You didn't even tell me that.

Thanks, I say.

She unfolds the paper. Her eyes scan the rows, working downward, her brow sloping with increasing severity.

She puts the paper down and looks at me dead on. You're taking my dad's position.

What do you mean? I ask, my voice wavering.

You're listed as Secretary Treasurer. That's my dad's position.

So he resigned?

No. No. My dad did not resign. He never said anything about it. He's a member of the board but your picture is here instead. What does this mean? She shows me the paper, my own face smiling back at me.

That's screwed up. We'll have to find out what happened. I try to pace myself, to answer with the right combination of nonchalance and concern. Yeah you know what, I don't know. I didn't know Vanek was going to do that. He just asked me if I wanted to be on the board.

What did he say when he asked you then? Did he mention my dad?

Ollie, come on.

So he did then?

Ollie, what are you saying I did?

Are you serious right now? Are you really helping Vanek get revenge on my dad? What is your deal, Graham?

She throws the paper on the ground.

Listen, Ollie, I'm sorry.

You know what, Graham, Ollie says, you're just selfish. You act like you're this thoughtful, introspective guy but you're just thinking about yourself the whole time. How does this dead painter relate to you? How does your boring hometown make you feel? How does getting a job affect you? How hard is your Ivy League life? You don't care about anyone else. I wish I could say I was disappointed, but now I'm realizing it all makes sense.

Ollie, please.

Graham, fuck off, she says finally raising her voice. She turns her back and starts walking away from me, I follow quickly calling her name.

Leave me alone. I'm going back to the hotel and I don't want to see you. That's it. Just get away from me, please. Her voice is calm again.

I stand still on the sidewalk and watch Ollie as she moves farther and farther away from me.

SUNDAY

Father Dubinsky: Please rise for the prayer. O Lord, save Thy people and bless Thine inheritance. Grant victories to the Orthodox Christians over their adversaries; and by the virtue of Thy Cross, preserve Thy habitation. As Thou was mercifully crucified for our sake, grant mercy to those who are called by Thy name; make all Orthodox Christians glad by Thy power, granting them victories over their adversaries, by bestowing on them the invincible trophy, Thy weapon of peace. For every good gift and every perfect gift is from above. Glory, thanksgiving, and worship to the Father, the Son, and to the Holy Spirit. Forever and ever and unto ages of ages.

All: Amen.

Dad: Please be seated. Roll call will be next.

Hubik: President Henry Vanek, here. Vice President Sergei Mercy, present.

Dad: Here.

Hubik: I'm here. Simon Hanek, Jr.

Hanek: Here.

Hubik: Auditor Martin M. Koval.

Martin Koval: Here.

Hubik: Auditor Matthew Korbel.

Korbel: Here.

Hubik: Michael S. Koval.

Michael Koval: Here.

Hubik: Director Arnold Levitski.

Levitski: Present.

Hubik: Director Gerald Malik, absent. Director Christopher Vanek.

Vanek: Here.

Hubik: Director Keith Witkiewicz.

Witkiewicz: Here.

Hubik: Thank you.

Dad: Sergeant at Arms? We're not ready yet? OK. Two minutes. Welp. First, a housekeeping announcement.

Check the bill for your room and if see if your $99 deposit was applied or not. If it wasn't first, at check-out, ask for Janet, who's an employee of the hotel and she'll check. And if not, Lauren will take care of it. She will check the rooms when she gets back to the office tomorrow. And if you have a problem call the office and we'll be sure to take care of it. So check your bill. There may be a couple of rooms where the $99 was not applied. That will be taken care of. Secondly, the ornaments that you received in your bag, which are really neat, we found them at the All-American Council a few years ago and ordered 100 — we got a special deal on them. But we have several left. If you're interested in purchasing them for yourself or for presents for friends or family, we have about a dozen left and they're $15, and you can see Natasha after the meetings. She has them in the storage room. Last, I have a report on what we raised at this event. We had the 50/50 winner donate her winnings to the scholarship fund, the basket raffle we raised $1,182, annuity scholarship drive we raised $2,265, and the scholarship drive we raised $3,065, for a total of $6,730 in scholarship

(*Applause.*)

I stayed up half the night. I stared at the ceiling thinking about what Ollie had said and contemplating what I should do, what changes I would have to make in order to make myself feel like some sort of good person. Turning down the role was probably the easiest option, but Vanek's pushback against me could be worse than his pushback against Phil Hubik. To kill a snake, you cut off its head. If I were to cross Vanek now he would surely attempt to do me in by way of my dad, firing or replacing him with impunity.

Despite having only slept a few hours, I'm wide awake before my alarm, already anxious for the day to start. This time it's uncertainty and anxiety that are slowing time down as I go over and over what I could do to fix the Vanek situation and, especially, what I might say to Ollie. Chances are she'll never talk to me again. I understand. I was in the wrong, I know it. That's fine, I accept my errors. I blew it, which is not unusual. It's not out of the ordinary. The narrative that I tried to claim was short-sighted, all rise and no resolution. And I desire resolution, I desire endings. I desired being able to look back and know that I did something. Now I'll pay the price.

I pull my T-shirt over my head and turn to the mirror to inspect myself before leaving for the last day of the convention. My cold sore persists, though due to constant application of Abreva it has almost crusted over entirely, a disgusting sight but a good sign. It's subsiding and soon it'll be gone.

But soon isn't soon enough.

I reach up and force a fingernail under the scab, wincing with slight pain as I force my finger farther forward, farther underneath. The scab starts to break away from my face, first in two small breaks and then in one giant chunk. Now there's no scab on my face. I sneeze three times almost immediately. I stare at myself in the mirror covered in snot, a dime-size bloody wound where the cold sore was.

I drive to Genetti's early and descend upon the familiar scene a final time: the breakfast buffet set up in the back of the room while people mull around talking casually and excitedly. There are no more meetings to sit through, no more facts and figures to be spit our way; we just have a short election and then everyone will be on their way, accruing 54 cents per mile and taking every toll road possible to increase the weight of their weekend's check.

Vanek stands at the back of the room, silent, in a small circle of other elderly men. He looks pleased. After the vote, the Organization will have returned to his complete control. He has order and he has it his way. No dissension. Everyone will be pleased. Despite the world's seeming to fall apart outside, the SBO's finances have under Vanek's leadership realized steady and reliable improvement, defying current economic sense and turning what had already been a supportive constituent base into devout believers. They were never given another choice.

Everyone here extends to the Slavic Brotherhood Organization a degree of care and concern that any objective observer would call misplaced. These people could afford to bury their dead loved ones with or without the SBO's modest payout. That goes for every last one of them, I would wager. No one here needs the marginal gains of a low-risk annuity. These are the baby boomers who made good on their parents' Depression-rooted status anxieties; they've found careers and passions and families, not to mention sufficient material security to support lifestyles that have maintained their belief, through thick and thin, in an increasingly rarified conception of the American Dream as we used to think of it: vaguely meritocratic but almost definitely certain.

The generation inheriting this moment, my generation, should be more concerned. America's shine has begun to wear off for us, and all we're left with is the knowledge that things aren't good and, in fact, may never have been good. We are the ones who will need funeral insurance, but we can't really consider that at the moment. I've got to get a lot more things done before I keel over and have my ashes dumped off the Market Street Bridge into the Susquehanna. Mainly get a job and figure out what I'm doing with the rest of my life. Really I have to *start* doing things finally. But first I have to sort out the current moment.

Ollie enters the room with the rest of her family. They are dressed down, car-driving clothes for an immediate departure. I can tell Ollie is purposefully not looking back at me. She knows I'm right here and, unfortunately for her, there's no way to avoid my presence this morning. Not if she wants the paycheck.

I don't want to approach her. I don't want to upset her. I also don't want to make a scene.

Instead of Ollie's gaze, I get Phil Hubik's glare. I can tell by the look that Ollie has told Phil what I've done, what I've committed to doing. His only recourse is to garner the public support that put him in his position four years ago, to rally the troops around his commonness. But this is not four years ago. This is now, and Vanek has learned from his missteps. There will be no nominations from the floor, there will be no testing of his power. If my election is the end result of the plan, I'm sure all of the steps before involving me were cautiously taken. The constituents were courted and measured.

My dad stands near the front of the room, looking over his notes for his last morning as convention chair. He sees me looking on and waves me over.

Hey, bud. Henry told me he's putting you on. That's great, you excited about it?

I don't think I want to do it anymore. I want to back out.

Why, what happened?

Vanek is only using me to get back at Phil Hubik. He wants him out. I just wanted a job, wanted to feel like I was becoming an adult.

Graham, I don't think you need this job or anything to be an adult. And if you don't want to do it, you don't have to. But that's not up to me. You have to talk to Vanek about that. You have to sort that out with him.

My dad puts his hand on my shoulder, consolatory and reassuring.

He said he would fire you if I told you, Dad.

He said what? Graham, I think he was just trying to intimidate you into taking the position. He's not going to fire me. Trust me. Just go talk to him.

I turn around and walk the opposite direction.

I approach Vanek, who's still soundlessly addressing a circle of courtiers.

Excuse me, Mr. Vanek. Can I ask you a quick question?

He nods, pulling away from his group.

Listen, Mr. Vanek, I'm really, really sorry . . . but I've had second thoughts and I'm wondering if you'd be all right if I back out. From the Executive Board, I mean.

Vanek leans into me, grabs my shoulder with surprising firmness, and speaks monotonously through his electric voice box.

NO, he says.

He takes out his pad and paper and, balancing them delicately on his left palm, begins to write out a message in his typical hurried scribble.

ITS TOO LATE TO BACK OUT NOW

I just feel bad about doing this to Mr. Hubik. I don't think it's right. I don't want the job, he does.

Vanek points past my head toward the rows of tables, on which his granddaughter is placing copies of the flyer he gave me yesterday. In front of every chair our printed faces lie supine, smiling at the ceiling. Vanek offers a brief smirk and a shrug before loosening his grip, patting me on the shoulder, and walking past me.

IT'S HIS FAULT, DON'T BLAME YOURSELF

My dad and I make eye contact from across the room and I shake my head, letting him know that I had no luck. Things were, as I expected, unchangeable.

At the table nearest the door, I see my mom sitting down enjoying her final meal. She waves at me. I simply nod in return.

Dad: Now, elections. Wait, first, actually, we should hear from the Grievance Committee.

Malik: The grievance committee is happy to report there are no grievances.

Dad: What are we paying you for? (*Laughter.*) OK, elections. The election of officers. Will the Nominating Committee please come up to the podium?

Wincheski: Good morning everybody.

All: Good morning.

Wincheski: All right, the Nomination Committee has met. For President, the Nomination Committee places the name of Henry Vanek.

Dad: The name of Henry Vanek has been placed in nomination for President. Are there any nominations from the floor? Any nominations from the floor? Hearing none, I close the nominations for President and declare Henry Vanek be instated as President by acclamation. All in favor?

All: Aye.

Dad: Opposed? None. Thank you. Congratulations.

(*Applause.*)

Wincheski: For Vice President, the Nominating Committee places the name of Sergei Mercy.

Dad: Thank you, I guess I'm running my own election here. Are there any nominations from the floor? Any nominations from the floor? Hearing and seeing none, and running unopposed, I name myself Vice President by acclimation. All in favor?

All: Aye.

Wincheski: For Auditor, the Nominating Committee places the names of Harold Vasko, Matthew Korbel, and Martin M. Koval.

Dad: Thank you, the names of Matthew Korbel, Martin Koval, and Harold Vasko have been placed in nomination for Auditor. Are there any nominations from the floor? Any nominations from the floor? Seeing and hearing none, I declare the three auditors by acclimation. And all those in favor?

All: Aye.

Dad: Thank you. There they are.

(*Applause.*)

Wincheski: For Directors, the Nominating Committee places the names of Michael Koval, Thomas Wincheski, and Gerald Malik.

Dad: Thank you. You've heard the names of Michael Koval, Thomas Wincheski, and Gerald Malik for Directors. Are there any nominations from the floor? Any nominations from the floor? Hearing and seeing no response, I declare them directors by acclimation. All in favor?

All: Aye.

(*Applause.*)

Wincheski: For Secretary Treasurer, the Nominating Committee places the name of Graham Mercy.

Dad: Thank you. The name of Graham Mercy has been placed for Secretary Treasurer. Any nominations from the floor? Any nominations from the floor? Seeing and hearing none, I declare Graham Mercy Treasurer by acclimation. All in favor?

All: Aye.

Dad: Thank you.

(*Applause.*)

Ollie stands in line for the buffet by herself, her family already seated. Her back is turned to me as I approach.

Hi Ollie, I say. I know you don't want to hear it but I just need to say I'm sorry. I'm really sorry for what I did. I tried to take it back, I tried to tell Vanek I didn't want it but he refused to listen.

Ollie doesn't turn around.

I didn't intend to hurt your feelings. I didn't even intend to take the job. Vanek threatened my dad's job and I got tied up in his plan. I made a big mistake and I know you're not going to forgive me but I want you to know that I realized what I did was wrong. I'm sorry.

She speaks without turning around. Graham, I don't really care. Even if you did back out now and get my dad his job back, I still wouldn't want to talk to you. I don't care about the SBO and I don't care about the dumb position but I do care about my family, and my dad cares about it and I care about him. I don't want your apology, I don't need it. What you're saying, it's devoid of meaning. I don't believe it. So please don't talk to me again, I don't want to hear it. Don't add me on Facebook and stalk me and tell me how sorry you are later, either. I don't care. Now please leave me alone.

Dad: We have now elected the slate of officers to lead us for the next four years, and according to our bylaws we will have our oath administered by our counsel, Andrew Sojka. So we're all up here, and — Graham come up here, please. That's everyone, correct? Great, we will stand and raise our right hand and the oath is administered as follows.

Sojka: I, state your name.

All: I, ___

Sojka: Do solemnly swear on my honor.

All: Do solemnly swear on my honor.

Sojka: That I shall faithfully and honorably perform my duty for office entrusted in me.

All: That I shall faithfully and honorably perform my duty for office entrusted in me.

Sojka: And I shall perform all the duties prescribed by the bylaws of the Organization.

All: And I shall perform all the duties prescribed by the bylaws of the Organization.

Sojka: And by all decisions of the convention.

All: And by all decisions of the convention.

Sojka: I shall with all my ability.

All: I shall with all my ability.

Sojka: Work for the interest and the progress of this Organization.

All: Work for the interest and the progress of this Organization.

Sojka: So help me God and the Holy Trinity.

All: So help me God and the Holy Trinity.

Sojka: God Bless the Virgin Mary.

All: God Bless the Virgin Mary.

Sojka: And all the saints.

All: And all the saints.

Sojka: Amen.

All: Amen.

I move silently away, across patterned carpet, and stand in the back of the room by myself waiting for the final moments of the convention to commence. Everything ran smoothly. Everyone seemed to enjoy themselves. And I managed to ruin it.

This whole time I had a picture in mind, a picture of my life as it would be once I finished school. And then once I moved back, and then once I got a job, and then once I moved out of my parents' — repeatedly changing the starting point every time I faced a new obstacle. It was supposed to be purposeful and pleasant and all that. I would get a job and I would do something meaningful and I would create meaning in my own and other people's lives by the work that I did. I would offer insightful things to say and would be respected. I would be loved by my partner, eventually my children, always my family. I would find meaning in all facets of my life. I was held captive by the picture. I wanted it so badly that I thought I was depressed because I couldn't see it as I wanted to see it. I thought I was sad because I was just waiting to be happy and the only way to reach that happiness was through the realization of these hopes and desires. Make that narrative real — my own, unique narrative. I couldn't realize it, though. I couldn't see this picture I was painting; it was so far away it was blurry. And now I tried to approach the picture and here I am. I got so close to it, but it was still just as blurry as it was from afar. Too close, I thought. I simply have to take a few steps back in order to truly visualize its massiveness. Now, here I am, realizing that the picture was just indistinct to begin with. Only now do I realize there wasn't anything to see in the first place.

The painting and its subject, what I've been working on my whole life, are empty.

And somehow it's still beautiful, I just didn't see it at the time.

Dad: It's too late to run, Michelle. (*Laughter.*) Welp, I think we've had a wonderful weekend, and, uh, we've got a wonderful group here. It's now that time to close with a prayer. So, Father Dubinsky.

Father Dubinsky: I have a little prayer here that I'd like to read, a paragraph from a longer prayer. It is entitled "Why Wait?"

The sad thing is that so many people under blue skies, fair winds, quiet seas, and calm days do not feel that unique sense that establishes their relationship with that which is basic in religion. Only when the storm breaks, death comes, illness overtakes us, or we lose our jobs, when we become hungry, do we cry, "I need the church, I need God." I know that this is a universal characteristic, but what I'd like to say is: if we cannot wait until we needed God but attempted immediately to get into our consciousness that perhaps God needs us now, we would build up a fortification, a barrier, impregnable and impervious to these admissions. It would do something for your health, your finances, your trouble, and happiness of your home. In the Lord's Prayer we speak of *our* daily bread, *our* trespasses, instead of saying, "My church, my creed, I, I, mine, mine," let us say, "Our God, our church, our life, our SBO, our nation, our world." Get the big theme, the sense of eternal life, get the sweep, the majesty, the sense of advance of the Eternal in your life. God, give me the sense of the Eternal.

Eternal and loving God, though the deep blue of Thy bountiful skies seems obscured and our hearts would automatically be chilled and our spirits depressed, we would express with exaltation and gladness the deep fault of our faith and our belief in the SBO, and in a certain knowledge that the sky is still blue, that love is still love, that it is still real. Oh Lord God, direct the steps of all the loving members of the SBO, their family members, and their friends, direct them this day to have a safe trip home. Amen.

All: Amen.

Dad: Thank you, Father. And, oh, one last bit of business:

I need a motion to adjourn the 25th Convention. All in favor?

All: Aye.

Dad: The convention is adjourned. We'll see you four years from now.

Thank you to the following people for their
ceaseless support and guidance:

My family, especially Mom and Dad, Sarah, my editor Matt
LaForge, John Scharbach and Zack Wuerthner from Shining
Life Press, Andrew Peden, Dave Nikityn, AJ McGuire, Lodewijk
Verduin, Sarah Gerard, Anelise Chen, Margaret Vandenburg,
and Will Evans.

Ned Russin is a musician and writer from Kingston, PA known for his work with the bands Title Fight and Glitterer. He is a graduate of Columbia University. This is his first novel.